Nothing Will Separate Us

Frederica de Graaf

Nothing Will Separate Us

Working Through the Suffering and Death of a Loved One

St. Nicholas Press

St. Nicholas Press is an imprint of the Road to Emmaus
Foundation. Publications may be purchased in
quantity for educational, business or promotional use.
For ordering information write or call:

St. Nicholas Press / Road to Emmaus Foundation
PO Box 198
Maysville, MO 64469

Phone and Fax: (+1) 816-449-5231
Email: stnicholaspress@gmail.com
Visit our website: www.stnicholaspress.net

ISBN: 978-1-63551-103-1
Library of Congress Control Number: 2019957077

Layout and Cover: Bruce Petersen Art Direction & Design

I am convinced that neither death nor life,
neither angels nor demons, neither the present
nor the future, nor any powers, neither height
nor depth, nor anything else in all creation,
will be able to separate us from the love of
God that is in Christ Jesus our Lord.

Romans 8:38-39

Nothing Will Separate Us

Working Through the Suffering and Death of a Loved One

Foreword

When I first spoke with Frederica de Graaf after decades of interviewing, I wondered if I had ever been listened to so deeply – without preoccupation, without composing a simultaneous answer, without emotion, motives and concerns as background noise – just a kindly waiting. Frederica listened not only to my questions but to me. Without intrusion, she just waited for what I had to offer.

I've often thought of that interview since, and in *Nothing Will Separate Us* Frederica offers her readers a way to communicate honestly without hard-edged rationalism and warmly without sentiment. This is a book of sober practicality shot through with the mindfulness of eternity.

Frederica deploys three great strengths. First, she draws on the words of the late Metropolitan Anthony Bloom of Sourozh, the Russian Orthodox primate of Great Britain and Ireland. Her own mentor and friend, Frederica introduces Met. Anthony as a physician, hierarch, and theologian who spent thousands of hours at the bedsides of the ill and dying, and whose clear-sighted reflections seed this book. One example will suffice:

> We need to train ourselves in such a way that we will be able to respond with all of our mind, all of our heart, but not to try (almost forcing ourselves from within a near-physical level) to feel the suffering which is not ours, or emotions which do not belong to us. The patient has no need of our living through his pain. He is in need of our creative responsiveness to his suffering and his condition. He is in need of a response that will put us into action, one which is in the first place rooted in respect, in reverence towards him….The worth of each person is expressed by the life and death of Christ.

Second, Frederica herself has nearly two decades of experience as a professional caregiver at the First Moscow Hospice, and has ministered to thousands of Russian patients and their relatives. As she recounts their stories, you understand that this rich and varied experience has become her own.

Finally, it is Frederica's Orthodox Christian faith in Christ's own victory over death that allows her to reflect with honest compassion on the physical, psychological, and spiritual needs of the dying and their relatives. Here, we are relieved of secular accounts of hospice care that would have us tip-toe around the bed saying nothing of eternal or personal significance because our aim is no higher than to make the dying person comfortable. While reminding us that we cannot speak from experience about what lies beyond death, Frederica shows how to dignify the emotional and spiritual needs of the dying and their relatives with clarity and faith.

Whether the reader has ever been at the bedside of an ill or dying relative, friend, or patient, or simply knows that such an experience will inevitably come his way, Frederica is an authentic and luminous guide. Her topics include our own relationship to suffering and death, the different stages in accepting a crisis, communicating with those who can and cannot speak, relations with relatives, dying children, the final hours, and living through loss and bereavement. Together, they give us a brilliant map of how to approach death with love, integrity, and faith. And in the end, this book is not about how to die but how to live.

Mother Nectaria (McLees)
Editor, *Road to Emmaus Journal*
August 4, 2018

Introduction

At the root of the medical attitude to the patient, to the problem of illness, to all the ethics and philosophy of medicine is this virtue of compassion, this sense of solidarity, this respect and veneration for human life, this devotion to the one person who is now in his presence. Short of this, the medical profession may be remarkably scientific, but it would lose its very substance.[1]

This book will deal with life in its fullest sense, life with depth and meaning, including life in the face of suffering and death. In essence, it is about Life and the preparation for a life where death does not exist. That is to say, a life where there will never be a separation, either from God or from our loved ones: "O death where is thy sting? O hell, where is thy victory?"[2] Christ is risen and death has been trampled down.

However, unless we incorporate into our own lives the only fact of which we are certain – that we all are mortal, that "I too will die" – then our own lives cannot fail to be fragmented and petty.

Orthodox Metropolitan Anthony of Sourozh has said more than once that as long as we are afraid of death, we will be afraid of living to the full. We will not live courageously or daringly and we will be afraid to take risks. It was his view that "we are all afraid of living seriously, with that joyful fullness of life which is rooted in love, in total openness of heart, without looking at oneself or at the possibilities of danger and death."

---

1 *Metropolitan Anthony of Sourozh*, "Human values in medicine." Delivered to the Bristol Medico-Chirurgical Society on 8th May 1974. Bristol Medico-Chirurgical Journal. Vol.91 (i/ii) 1976. http://masarchive.org/Sites/texts/1974-05-08-1-E-R-T-EM05-037HumanValuesInMedicine.html

2 Hosea 13:14.

In one of his talks, Vladika Anthony spoke of death as follows:

> Death for me, and I am certain that this is so in general, is the cornerstone of our attitude towards life. People who are afraid of death are afraid of life. It is impossible not to fear life with all of its complexities, its dangers, and with life's total and ultimate risk, when there is the fear of death. To solve the problem of death is not at all of little importance. If we fear death, we will go through life cowardly, carefully, and timidly. Only when we can look death straight in the face, find our own attitude towards it, and live daringly, will we be able to live our life to the full.... [3]

In Vladika Anthony's experience, this does not relate only to the death of our body. According to him, we must learn to be ready to face death in all of its aspects, including the "death" that comes with being rejected or forgotten. In his opinion, it is of prime importance for us to learn to "let go" – to die to our old selves in order to become what we are now or what we are called to be. He goes on to explain that one day we will discover that we are no longer children, and not even "grown-up" people anymore, but that we have grown old. If we desperately cling to the past, if we try to remain the same as we always were, we will never be able to become real in the present. It is very important to find in oneself the strength to let go of that which used to be dear and well known in order to be open to something new, something often not yet visible. This relates not only to having to let go of a dear person before his death, but also circumstances in our daily life that are bound to change.

This book is about how our contemporaries – both children, adults, and their relatives – relate and react to serious illness, dying, and death. It also gives examples of how, within faith or in the absence of it, patients have entered eternal life.

3 *Antonij mitr. Surozhskij.* Bog v nas verit. Moskva: Pravoslavnoe bratstvo sv. apostola Ioanna Bogoslova, 2010 (Russian) *Metropolitan Anthony of Sourozh*, "On Death," from the website of Metropolitan Anthony of Sourozh. Archive: http://masarchive.org/Sites/texts/1978-00-00-1-E-E-T—EW00-010OnDeath.html

This book has been written in the hope that if we can begin to live life in all of its depth and fullness through our acceptance of our own mortality, we will realize what a precious gift life is. Only then will it be possible for us not to regret how we have lived at the end of our lives. If this happens, then no one will have to say: "I have not yet begun to really live!"

First, I want to remember with deep gratitude my spiritual guide Metropolitan Anthony of Sourozh, a physician of body and soul, who by his example and teaching brought me to the source of life: to Christ.

When Vladika Anthony was still very young, his father once told him that it should be of no importance whether he lived or died. What mattered was what he was ready to live and die for. It was by this advice that Vladika Anthony lived his entire life until his death in 2003.

I would also like to thank my teachers of acupuncture, Dr. J. van Buren and his wife P. van Buren, who for many years have taught and shared their experience and deep knowledge of this field of medicine with me. It is thanks to them that I am now able to treat and alleviate the suffering of many of my patients.

I am grateful to Archpriest Alexis Zotov who was in charge of the Church of Sts. Florus and Laurus in Moscow. For more than ten years, right up until his death, Archpriest Alexis prayed with deep joy for all of my patients, both for the living and for the souls of those who had died.

I also wish to thank Archpriest Nicholas Konovalov, who still serves in this same church, and who blessed me to write this book.

Certainly, I owe a deep debt of gratitude to all of my patients and their relatives, in England and in Russia, whom I have met over the past twenty-five years. These are the people who, by their example and struggle, by their fear and courage, have allowed me to witness to the fact that the last word is not death, but Life.

I am also indebted to all of those who relentlessly urged me to write down my experience of working with the terminally ill, particularly to Boris Sergeevich Bratus and Natalya Inina for their precious remarks and advice over the final drafts of this book.

Very special thanks goes to Maria Grausman, for without her efficient and joyful help this book would not have been written. For this English edition, a great thank you is due to Tatiana Pantchenko, who inspired and made it possible for me to have a quiet place for translating the Russian version into English.

My gratitude also goes out to Bruce Clark, who corrected my English in the draft of this translation from the Russian text.

– Frederica de Graaf

CHAPTER ONE

How We Relate to Suffering and Death

Is Suffering Always Evil?

How can one relate to suffering, not running away from it or denying its existence? How can one confront suffering face to face?

Metropolitan Anthony of Sourozh speaks about suffering as follows: one of the reasons why we are so at a loss when faced with suffering (not only of adults but, in particular, the suffering of children) is because we do not have our own point of view, our own criteria of suffering. We are often confronted with it unexpectedly, without having previously thought out how we relate to suffering in general.

Nowadays, it is commonly thought that suffering is a mere evil to be avoided, alleviated at all costs, and if possible, removed totally. This, I think, leads to cowardice: people fear suffering and at times this fear is more crippling than the actual suffering itself.

Metropolitan Anthony:

> In order to face suffering, one must have a daring and manly attitude to life. If we start with the assumption that life must be easy, that suffering must be absent from it, that what matters is that I should continue to live and to receive from life all the enjoyment it can give, then to face suffering is extremely difficult.
>
> If I live for something, if I am prepared to die for something, if for me there are values greater than myself, issues that are more

important than what happens to me, I have a framework and I can face suffering. You may say that this is a heroic attitude. No, it is not. It is the attitude that each of us has in regard to a limited number of commitments or relationships.

We are easily prepared to face and endure suffering for one person…. This shows that even at the lowest ebb of our ability we possess the capacity to face suffering if we can only connect it to values that we are prepared to serve or to people who matter enough for us to forget ourselves. At this point, whether we think of God or whether we think of other people, one of the decisive words is neither duty nor courage, but love.[4]

Here is an example that illustrates Vladika Anthony's words:[5]

In our hospice was a mother, Irina, with her little five-year-old boy, Johnny, who had been diagnosed with a brain tumor. As a result of the tumor, he had gone blind and his mother stayed with him day and night, never even going out into the garden. Although physically and emotionally exhausted, the condition of her child had become more important to her than her own well-being. One day she said to me: "I could never have dreamed that it would be possible to stay so long with my child, almost without sleep and rest for so many years."

Irina became extremely tired, but for Johnny's sake she kept going until the end. She was always near him and did everything she could to make things easier for him. She knew that he was dying, but in spite of her deep sorrow she managed to remain collected. Irina was very open and forthcoming, and all of the medical personnel grew to love her. She told me that, although baptized, she rarely went to church: "I have my own faith and relationship with God."

4 *Metropolitan Anthony of Sourozh*, "On Facing Suffering," an address given in the University Church of St. Mary the Virgin, Oxford, February 1st 1969. http://masarchive. org/Sites/texts/1969-02-01-1-E-E-T-EM01-077OnFacingSuffering(Medical).html

5 All of the names in the following examples have been changed.

Finally, Johnny slipped into a coma and lay for many days with his eyes closed. Irina and I were sitting next to him when, suddenly, not long before he died, he regained consciousness, and looked up at the ceiling with radiant eyes. His lips were moving and it was clear that he was talking to someone. Both Irina and I watched, holding our breath. After half an hour, Johnny closed his eyes and sank back again, descending deep into himself.

I left Irina for a short while to allow her to be on her own with her little son. When Johnny was close to death, we waited together next to his bed with his mother holding his hand. When he breathed his last, I heard her barely audible words: "Thank you, God".

Late that evening, Irina and I sat together, and it was then that she said to me: "Do you remember how Johnny was talking to someone we could not see shortly before he died? After you left, I said to him: 'Johnny, if you are now with our sweet God, then take Him by the hand. I will let you go.'" Soon after, he died.

Irina was able to totally forget about herself for the sake of her son. She had learned to live for something (or in this case, someone) that mattered more than her own peace of body and soul; and she did this over a long period of time. In spite of her own deep suffering, she did not think of herself; her only wish was to alleviate her son's suffering. For me this was an inspiring example of sacrificial love.

Here is another example which shows that suffering has meaning and is far from merely being evil:

In our hospice there was a young woman called Anna. She had a husband and a little six-year-old daughter who, during Anna's illness, was looked after by her grandmother. Now, Anna was a Muslim; she was intensely alive and a great beauty. One day she said to me: "I used to live just as all the young people live nowadays. I was very cruel, I worked in order to get more and more money, and I treated my husband badly. I wanted him to provide me with a luxurious house and a lot of money. Then I started drinking with friends, even though at the same time I knew that I was perishing. I desperately wanted to change and live in a different way, but I could not. My soul was crying out to God and I asked Him not to leave me altogether.

Then I suddenly became seriously ill with breast cancer and, while struggling to come to terms with my illness, I slowly began to understand that God loves me. I changed completely, I have become another person, and now I pray in my own words. Of course, I still suffer and I am anxious about my little daughter. I discuss everything with her; there are no secrets between us. I hide nothing from her."

Anna was discharged from the hospice to go to live with her relatives in the south of Russia. It was especially important for her to be with her deeply beloved father. Anna lived another two months, having become a different person thanks to her illness.

Is Death Always an Evil?

As long as we have not determined our attitude towards our own death, the fear of death will inevitably be with us in all that we do; it will color everything we undertake. However, if there is always a "remembrance of death" inside of us, it is precisely this state of mind that allows us to discover the meaning and importance of each moment of life. For instance, when a person close to us is dying, any word spoken may be the last he hears, and with this word he will enter into eternity.

In regard to this Vladika Anthony said: "Death, the thought of it and its remembrance, is the only thing that gives life a higher meaning."[6] In his experience, it is precisely a serious illness that gives us the possibility to become ourselves, to let go of false masks,

6 Antonij mitr. Surozhskij, "Zhizn'. Bolezn'. Smert'.: Cennost' vremeni." (Moskva: Fond Duhovnoe nasledie Mitropolita Antoniya Surozhskogo, 2010) (Russian) [Metropolitan Anthony of Sourozh, "Life. Illness. Death: The Value of Time." Moscow: Metropolitan Anthony of Sourozh Spiritual Foundation, 2010. Talks given by Metropolitan Anthony April-May, 1984 at the Russian Cathedral in Ennismore Gardens, London.]

of all that is negative in ourselves, the feelings of guilt and of being offended. However, this is not only true for patients and their relatives but equally so for each one of us in daily life. I often hear from patients that thanks to their illness they have begun to look at life differently, that there has been a radical change of values.

I feel it is also important to avoid looking at illness and death as a personal defeat, as did one young patient who said: "I am a failure, I was not able to fight my illness." On the contrary, a well-known Russian priest, Father John Krestiankin, has said that a serious illness can be seen as a "last exam." This raises the question of how to prepare for it.

Vladika Anthony answers this as follows:

> Our days are not what they seem to be, time is illusory. If we say that we should remember death, this does not mean that we should fear life. This is said so that we should live with all our intensity, all our might, as we would if we were aware that each moment is a unique one for us.
>
> Each moment of our life should be perfect not only at the receding of the wave but at its crest; it should not be defeat but victory. However, when I speak of defeat and victory, I do not have in mind either outward success or its absence. I have in mind an inner becoming, an inner growth, the ability to be at each given moment all that one is in all of his fullness.[7]

During a serious illness our attitude towards death will undoubtedly influence our physical, emotional, and spiritual condition. If there is nothing in ourselves to fall back on, no inner "crutch" or support when faced with suffering, it will probably be hard for us to look at the situation directly. If seen as the end of everything, fear of death may take hold of us completely unless we

7 Antonij mitr. Surozhskij, "Zhizn'. Bolezn'. Smert'.: 'Pamyat' smertnaya'" (Moskva: Fond Duhovnoe nasledie Mitropolita Antoniya Surozhskogo, 2010) (Russian). [Metropolitan Anthony of Sourozh, "Life. Illness. Death: Remembrance of Death." (Moscow: Metropolitan Anthony of Sourozh Spiritual Foundation, 2010)] Talks given by Metropolitan Anthony on April-May, 1984 at the Russian Cathedral in Ennismore Gardens, London.

have this inner spiritual experience, the confidence that life will continue after death, that death opens wide the gates to Life.

Different Attitudes Towards Death

Vladika Anthony discerns three types of people, each with a different attitude towards death.

The first type is the person who is a staunch atheist, totally convinced that there is no life after death whatsoever. This person will die calmly. However, in Vladika Anthony's long life experience as a doctor and a priest, he said that he had never met such a radical unbeliever. The second type he calls the person who has only "a quarter" of belief. This person has been baptized, but the fact that Christ became one of us by taking on our flesh in His Incarnation means little to him. Nor does the reality of the Resurrection make any difference to his own daily life: therefore, it does not change his view on illness and death.

Sadly, I have to say that in my experience most people I have met fall into this type. Often, after suddenly falling seriously ill they ask, "Why me, What for? I have always been a good person; I have never harmed anyone. Why does God punish me now?" This type of person often behaves towards his illness in a timid or resentful way. He feels that he is a victim of "fate," and this often results in a refusal to take responsibility for his life, including his attitude towards his illness and death.

Vladika Anthony regards death from a Christian point of view as a direct result of the Fall, that is, original sin. At the moment our first parents turned away from God, death appeared in the world, and we continue this even now. Death exists because we live in a fallen world not in full communion with God.

As a physician of body and soul, Vladika Anthony stresses how important it is when one has become seriously ill, to be concerned not only with healing of the body but also of the soul:

On the one hand, illness is connected with the common destiny of man, with the weakening of mankind as a whole, with the fact that we all are mortals and that we are exposed to suffering and death. On the other hand, illness is connected with what is happening in our soul. As soon as a person has fallen ill, he should first of all go inward and look at himself to see how far he is removed from God, what kind of untruth there is in his relation to the people close to him, in relation to himself, and also to what extent he defiles and disfigures the image of God in himself.

After and together with this, he should humbly seek and endure the doctor's treatment without relying upon his own strength, thinking that, by his "miraculous repentance," he can heal himself of his physical illness.[8]

As a psychiatrist himself, Vladika Anthony had this to say regarding mental illness:

We know now that the state of the psyche depends to a great extent on what is happening physiologically – from the point of view of physics and chemistry – in our brain and in our nervous system. This is why we should not attribute a mental illness to evil, sin, or the devil. Very often, mental illness is a result of an imbalance in the nervous system, rather than provocation by an attack of the devil or as a result of a sin which has torn away all bonds with God. Here the medical professional comes into his own right and can do a great deal to help.[9]

What about the third type of person and his attitude towards illness and death? This is the person who really believes, who has come to know the risen Christ from his own inner experience. For him, death becomes a mere falling asleep and a transition

8 Antonij mitr. Surozhskij, "Stupeni: O bolezni dushevnoj i telesnoj." *Besedy mitropolita Antoniya Surozhskogo.* S. Reshma: Izd.Makariev-Reshemskoj obiteli, 1998 (Russian) [Metropolitan Anthony of Sourozh, "Steps: About Mental and Physical Illness," *Talks of Metropolitan Anthony of Sourozh* (Ivanovo, Edition of Makaryev-Reshemsky Monastery, 1998).]

9 ibid.

into another world, the world of eternity. During his illness he is preparing for the joyful meeting with Christ.

As an example of the first type of person, we can look at Socrates who courageously looked death in the face. However, in Vladika Anthony's opinion, for Socrates death meant the end of life. Death therefore won; it had not been overcome.

As an illustration of this second type, I would like to mention one of our hospice patients named Lidia:

From the very first day until the last, Lidia cried bitterly about her terminal illness. She herself had been a pediatrician, but in no way would she accept the fact that she was now going to die. Her sister came every day to visit her and did all she could to provide comfort but to no avail. Lidia rejected everything she was offered. Nothing was right, neither the delicacies her sister brought her nor any other kind of support. Eventually she died. I think the surviving sister will always remember the way Lidia behaved and how she died, and this may have a direct impact on the way she faces her own death.

This example shows so clearly how we have a responsibility to the people left behind. It is by our example that we can inspire others for the future. We can give courage to the people near us, thus preparing them for the moment when they will have to face their own illness and death.

Here is another instance of how a person of this second type reacts to the death of a loved one:

Peter stayed in our hospice only for a short time. He was nineteen years old and had been diagnosed with lung cancer. His mother refused point blank to look honestly at what was happening with her son. As a result, Peter was left completely alone. He had to face his fears and coming death by himself, on his own. He knew that he was going to die, but in no way was he allowed to talk about it. (In my experience, all patients know about it when they are going to die, even if they do not say so.)

In this case, none of Peter's relatives had the courage to join him in facing up to what was happening. Peter was left to deal with his sorrow and suffering without any support, and this made his symptoms worse, especially his breathing. What made matters even worse was that his relatives did not allow anyone else to approach the subject of his illness and death with him.

The cause of his suffering was not only his physical condition but to a very great extent the fact that he was left alone without emotional support. His mother (although a doctor herself) out of her own deep-seated fear was unable to touch him and thus convey her love to him without words; she seemed to be frozen. Only when she saw that her son was breathing his last did the ice break. At the top of her voice she began shouting, "No, Peter, no!" Only then could she embrace him, but he had already died. Only then was she able to get in touch with her feelings, her fear, and her own suffering. She told me angrily that she no longer could believe in a God who would let her son suffer so much!

When there is anger and protest against God at the moment of deep crisis, this anger is simply an expression of unbearable pain. Vladika Anthony says, "At times a person behaves badly and even does something malicious, simply because there is such acute pain that this is the only way he can express it."[10] He adds that if the anger is directed towards God, that He certainly will be able to take it.

Here is another example of a young person, but one who was clearly of the third type:

10 Antonij mitr. Surozhskij, "Nachalo Evangeliya Christa, Syna Bozhiya... Besedy na Evangelie ot Marka". Moskva: Danilovskij blagovestnik, 1998 (Russian) [Metropolitan Anthony of Sourozh, "The Beginning of the Gospel of Jesus Christ, the Son of God...: Talks on the Gospel according to Saint Mark." Moscow: *Danilovsky Evangelist*, 1998.]

Michael was twenty-two years old. He was admitted to the hospice with progressive sarcoma of his leg. His condition slowly deteriorated and he began to be short of breath. Day and night his wife stayed with him in a room they had to themselves. Both of them regretted that they had not yet had any children, but it was Michael's dream to at least have a little kitten, and very soon the dream was fulfilled. The kitten immediately found its place on the bed close to him and fell asleep, completely relaxed. During his illness and in spite of his suffering, Michael only thought of the well-being of others; all of his care and thoughts were directed to them.

He knew his diagnosis; he knew he was going to die. He totally believed and was convinced that death was not the end, that he would meet his wife again. I asked him whether he had had a personal experience of life after death. He said: "No, but for me the words in Scripture are enough: "I am the God of Abraham, the God of Isaac, and the God of Jacob…. God is not the God of the dead, but of the living."

Michael and his wife spoke openly about his coming death. Michael thought that it was his responsibility to continue to defend and care for his wife while he was alive, and he was sure that he would continue looking after her after his death. I feel that for Michael, facing up squarely to his illness, grief, and coming death made his suffering much easier to bear. I also consider that through his deep faith in life after death, he had indeed conquered death. Eventually, he peacefully and quietly entered into that eternal Life whose existence had been such a reality and support to him and his wife during his illness. In spite of her pain, his wife accompanied Michael in an equally dignified way through every step of his illness. Their love for each other, and their deep conviction that their separation would only be temporary, gave them the strength to face everything with admirable courage. They were together until the very end, and their many friends were a great support to them.

A terminal illness can be the start of looking at life with different values. This is something I have seen in my own family. My sister, who was herself a doctor, was unexpectedly diagnosed with cancer of the bowel and secondary tumors in the liver. The doctors gave her three months to live. I believe that it was thanks to her positive attitude that she lived another seven months. Each day she spent a long time in silence on her own, trying to look at herself and her life. She strove to examine herself and what had been going on within her. She was fully aware that the body and soul are closely interconnected.

Not long before her death she said to me: "I am not a cancer patient, I am myself, only with a problem." She was determined to live as normal a life as possible, only with some limits due to her illness. Although she was already very ill, she made a plan to go to see her spiritual guide, who lived abroad. When I asked her how things would be if she were to die on the way, she simply replied, "What will happen will happen. I will have a friend with me who is a doctor; she has promised to take care of me."

A week before her death, I spoke to her by phone from Russia. She told me that she was extremely grateful to all of the people who were taking care of her, and who had made it possible for her to remain at home. She was inviting them all to come and see her at the end of the following week. She said, "If I get tired, I will lie down for a little while, and then we will be all together." I remember her last words to me: "You know, when you stand in front of death, everything changes." She had in mind the ability at that point to forgive totally, to accept all that had happened in her life in the light of her coming death. Sadly, she was not given the chance to meet all of the people she had invited to come; she died two days before the time she had proposed.

I am convinced that these examples are relevant not only to the terminally ill and their relatives, but to any person who is facing a serious crisis. Our own attitude towards a crisis will have a great impact on its outcome; much is determined by how we deal with our fears and relate to the complex reality of life.

Different Approaches of the Medical Staff and Patients' Relatives to Terminal Illness

If doctors or nurses themselves experience fear in the face of death, then they will never be able to help a patient who is dying. As long as a medical professional has not accepted the fact that he or she is also going to die and has not yet found a way of dealing with death, that caregiver's hidden fears will, without doubt, have repercussions on patients and their treatment.

In these situations, the behavior of the professionals will be obstructed by multiple defenses, both on the physical and on the psychological level. For example, on the physical level the professionals may experience a lack of energy, sudden back pain, migraines, or anything that supposedly "prevents" them from staying for any length of time with a dying patient.

On the psychological level, professionals sometimes show a reluctance to be serious. They may engage in superficial chatter to avoid exposing any vulnerability, or they may claim to be too busy to sit silently with a patient. This is a pity because it is in the space given by deep silence that a patient can open up and discuss their fears frankly. Consciously or unconsciously, these defense mechanisms, this refusal to engage with a patient's pain and suffering, may reflect a worry that the sick individual will bring up the subject of imminent death and ask awkward questions; questions that can only be answered in a spirit of readiness to share the patient's agony.

These defense mechanisms, this blocking out of the reality of suffering and death, can take other forms. For example, doctors may refuse to stop active treatment even when the patient is already dying. At times, the medical profession will not accept that nothing more can be done other than palliative care. On the other hand, relatives may not be able to accept this hard reality, and this often comes at a cost for the patient. It may be that the situation has not been properly explained to them, or there may be a deep-seated fear of facing the real facts.

Relatives sometimes insist on continuing active treatment at all costs, even when this prolongs the patient's suffering, and this can even be seen in the hospice setting. I have met relatives who insisted on transferring an already dying patient by ambulance to an intensive care unit in a different hospital. I feel strongly that in such cases the doctors should take time to explore the relatives' fears and ascertain the motives for their requests. They should then explain the suffering and harm that such pointless intervention will cause the patient.

It can also happen, even when a patient is clearly close to the end, that relatives will insist on pretending that all is fine. They try to cheer the patient up with dishonest words: "You are looking well. You see, you are already getting better." This can create a wall of falsehood and deceit between patient and relative. As a result, the patient is left in total isolation, with no choice but to stay silent and play the game.

Although the patient's body is getting weaker, life forces are dwindling, and he is fully aware that death is coming, he is left in utter loneliness to endure pain and face the coming end. We have already seen how Peter was left alone to face his death because of his relatives' deep-seated fear. This made it impossible for them to support him or to join him in preparing for the life he was about to enter, although Peter himself knew that the end was near.

Every time such a wall of falsehood is erected, the patient closes down and, more often than not, will not find an opening to speak about his fears, anxieties, and sorrow. As a result, not only his physical state but also his emotional and spiritual symptoms are bound to get even worse.

However, we have seen the opposite in the example of Michael: how the honesty and openness of the people around him were of great support to him in facing everything courageously.

Thus, the attitude of relatives toward what is happening has a direct and deep influence on the physical, emotional, and spiritual state of the patient.

CHAPTER TWO

The Patient and His Condition

The Challenge of Becoming Human

In this chapter I would like to recall Viktor Frankl, a neurologist and psychiatrist who worked in Vienna before the Second World War. As Jews, he and his whole family were deported to concentration camps. He survived three years in various camps and later described his experiences with the different people he met there, and how they reacted towards the cruel and exhausting conditions they endured. He wrote that the majority of the people in the camps simply tried to survive at any cost; their thoughts were centered on how to obtain another piece of bread.

However, Frankl occasionally met people who were different. These were the ones who, in spite of the horrific conditions in the camps, found a meaning in something far beyond themselves. They were able to go beyond their immediate circumstances and live for something greater. They found this meaning in beauty, in a deep love for someone, or in their love of God.

Frankl was convinced that people have to take responsibility for their attitude to the fundamentals of life, including serious illness and death. In my experience, this is absolutely true. People do make a choice, either to become victims of their "destiny" or to accept that suffering is an opportunity for growth, a growth that comes as one's experience of life deepens. Depending on how we choose to respond to our fate, and ultimately to our death, we can either surrender to an existential vacuum or experience a sense of growth in inner freedom.

During his time in the concentration camp, Frankl came to the following conclusion. The most important question a person has to face in life is not so much, "How can I survive?" but "What is worth living for?" (This is similar to the advice given to the youthful Vladika Anthony by his father.)

Frankl was also of the opinion that the real question should be: "What can I still give in life?" rather than "What can I get out of life?" He quotes Nietzsche's words: "He who has a why to live for can bear with almost any how."[11]

As we have noted, Frankl sees several ways of finding meaning in life: through creating something, through the appreciation of beauty, and through love. Yet another way lies in consciously determining one's attitude to a situation which is beyond our control, such as terminal illness. Frankl is adamant that even in situations of apparent helplessness, a person can find meaning. When we cannot change the circumstances, we are called on to change ourselves.

As Frankl sees it, everything depends on the attitude that a person adopts in the face of a destiny that cannot be changed or avoided. By adopting the right attitude, we can demonstrate the heights that mankind is capable of reaching. In this way we can change and transform suffering into an achievement worthy of mankind's highest calling.

In Frankl's opinion, there is no situation in life which is devoid of meaning: "When a person has found meaning in his life, he will realize himself. When man has discovered for himself the meaning of suffering, then the most human aspect of man will have come to life."[12] Frankl also mentions a friend who after surviving the camp came to realize a deep truth: suffering only has meaning if, as a result, the sufferer becomes a different person.

11 Viktor E. Frankl, *Man's Search for Meaning.* New York: Washington Square Press, 1985, p. 97.

12 *Frankl*, ibid.

I would like to make a similar point with the example of Xenia, a young patient of ours in the hospice. When I asked what she had learned from her illness and if something had changed in her, she answered:

I have found my faith again in people and in God. I am so grateful to have met so many good people. There is in me now something of a child who has become trusting and more open and perhaps a little more goodness towards myself and others. As regards my illness, I am at peace; there is no anger any more, just a little more humility. I have let go of all of my old grudges and I feel so light within. On the whole, I have come to love and appreciate life more. I have come to the conclusion that one has to live in harmony with oneself and that one has to turn to the doctors in time.

In this we see how Xenia has become whole. In speaking of wholeness, Vladika Anthony asks a hard question: Does a person want to be healed only in order to continue the previous way of life that caused him to fall apart in body and soul? Or does he want to lead another life, a life of wholeness?

Wholeness to Vladika Anthony meant living in harmony with God, which in his view was even more important than physical health. It was his opinion that if wholeness is given together with physical health, this is fine, but if this is not the case it can still be a great gift that helps a person to be in tune with God.

Frankl talks about a woman in the concentration camp who knew that in a few days she was going to die. In spite of this, she was cheerful. "I thank my fate, which has been so severe with me," she said. "This is because in my life I have been very spoiled, and my spiritual endeavors were not serious."

In Vladika's experience, when someone takes up the challenge of accepting suffering and evil, this person will change: "He will without doubt grow into a totally different dimension. There will be greatness if he is able to openly encounter any suffering, hatred, sorrow, or horrors of war, and yet remain human. He will become even greater, let us say, when he is able to acquire compassion, understanding, courage, and the readiness to give and to sacrifice himself."[13]

In this connection, I would like to quote a twenty-nine-year-old Jewish woman who lived in the Netherlands. Etty Hillesum died in the gas chambers of the Auschwitz concentration camp in 1943. It was her dream to become a writer and in her diary of the camp she described her feelings thus:

> Suffering has always been with us. Is it really of any importance what form it takes? The only thing that matters is how we ourselves take it, live through it, and make it a part of our life. At times I bow my head before the heavy burden which hangs over me. However, as soon as I let my head drop, at the same time, almost inevitably, I experience the need to pray. And I can sit so for hours and know everything. I become stronger and stronger while accepting what is happening; and yet at the same time with all my being, I believe that life is beautiful, has a meaning, and is worth living.[14]

Etty Hillesum belonged to the third type of a person: she defeated death, and we have testimonies from camp survivors that on the way to the gas chambers she and her companions departed singing, and that Etty supported the people around her.

Frankl was convinced that man cannot but search for meaning in his life. This, in his view, is man's deepest longing, something which cannot be taken away. Moreover, the question of meaning stands out in all its sharpness in circumstances where it seems that "matters cannot be worse" – as is the case in a concentration camp or when death is imminent. This question of meaning can also arise, acutely, in situations where restlessness has come to an end, and there is space and time to pause and ponder the significance of life.

13 Antonij mitr. Surozhskij, "Dialog veruyushchego s neveruyushchim," v religioznoj programme Bi-Bi-Si. 1972 (Russian). [Metropolitan Anthony of Sourozh, "Dialogue of a Believer with an Unbeliever," for BBC religious program, 1972, London.]

14 Etty Hillesum, *An Interrupted Life: The Diaries, 1941-1943* (New York: Pantheon Books, 1983).

As Frankl saw, a man's life should be orientated towards something or someone which is not himself. That is, towards something meaningful which then has to become a reality, or towards a person to whom he is attached in love. Frankl was convinced that in serving a particular purpose or in showing one's love for someone we become ourselves and find meaning. He was certain that searching our conscience would make it possible for us to find the one and only real meaning which is hidden in any situation.

Frankl wrote that man is not here on earth to look only at himself or to reflect his own needs. He is here in order to serve, to deny himself, and in the course of coming to know himself, to sacrifice that self with love.

In extreme environments, such as in a concentration camp or when living through terminal illness, the question of human personality comes acutely to the fore. It is Frankl's experience that no one can survive without hope. He said that if one "loses the inner structure of planning in time," this will often lead to a feeling of emptiness and a fatal loss of meaning. As he put it, the person who has no faith in the future, in his own future, will be the one who dies in the camp. Such a person without spiritual support will allow himself to decline inwardly. This inner breakdown also results in a physical surrender.

Frankl came to the conclusion that the question of meaning in extreme situations is ultimately a question about the meaning of death. In his view, it is only when a person has solved this question for himself that he can live as a real person who is no longer dependent on or determined by external circumstances.

Learning to "Be"

One of the most difficult tasks for each of us is to learn to "be," instead of endlessly "doing" with constant activity. When a person falls seriously ill and ordinary life falls apart, this is one of the most trying challenges – to find peace in being alone with oneself and drawing on what lies within. It is on that basis that a person must relate to the world around him.

People often ask: "How can I learn to 'be myself' with no external distractions?" To help answer this, I will introduce Alexander, a member of our London parish who, prior to becoming seriously ill, frequently complained to Vladika Anthony that he was always so busy that he never could find the time to stop, to be still and look at his life:

One day after a routine checkup at the hospital, Alexander was told that he had advanced cancer of the liver and did not have long to live. He met Vladika Anthony and complained that although he had so much to do, now he was physically unable to accomplish anything. Vladika simply reminded him that he had always been frustrated by his inability to make time stand still; now God had done exactly that for him. Instead of perpetually running, he advised Alexander to learn to "be."

Alexander did not know what this meant or what to do, but in the following weeks they worked at this together. As a physician and a priest, Vladika understood from experience how close the relationship is between the body and the soul, and how all "negative" emotions: feelings and thoughts of hatred, anger, fear, or grudges drain our life energies. So, together they spent a period of time looking over what was not yet "quite right," not yet resolved deeply in Alexander's soul. They looked at his life, which had been a long and difficult one. They examined his thoughts, feelings, and deeds, starting at the present time and going further and further into the past weeks, months, and years – as far back as Alexander could remember. After having courageously relived these moments of his past and having acknowledged both the things for which he had to ask forgiveness and the things he had to forgive, he made his peace with everyone, with himself, and with God. In this way, he let go of everything that had been burdening his soul.

Vladika Anthony told us that when Alexander was very close to death and too weak to hold a cup, he looked up from his bed and said: "I feel weak as never before, and yet I have never felt myself so intensely alive."

To my mind, this example shows us how important it is to learn simply to "be" when, because of a serious, incapacitating illness, a person is no longer able to live as actively as before. One has to make a patient aware of this imperative and help him to accept it as a challenge posed by his illness. The patient needs to understand that resolving this matter will have a deep impact on the state of his body and of his soul. This challenge is important because it is so closely linked to the meaning of suffering.

We have seen how, in Frankl's view, each person is responsible for determining his attitude to a destiny which cannot be avoided, to a fate that cannot be changed. As we have discussed, there is a choice between simply being a victim and striving instead for inner growth and freedom. We have seen how such a choice influences the physical, emotional, and spiritual state of the patient, who will either experience an existential vacuum or find meaning in suffering and the prospect of death.

Illness and Guilt

Viktor Frankl also wrote about the triad of suffering, guilt, and death: When there is utter despair, we cannot find happiness, but we can still live and be guided by a strong sense of meaning. Man, he said, is not a victim but takes part in shaping his destiny, and this is why he must take responsibility for what is happening. Real freedom is not freedom "from something" but a freedom "towards something"; towards certain aims, tasks, and accomplishments in life. A person may not be free to determine what is happening to him (these may be circumstances beyond his control), but he is free to shape his attitude to the situation he is in. Often, we cannot change the objective cause of suffering, but we can change how we relate to it.

Frankl also talks about the feelings of guilt which may come over a person who is facing death. He advises, first of all, that one should recognize and accept guilt for what it is, without trying to make excuses for oneself by pretending "I am not really to blame." Then, he says one should make peace with the person towards whom one feels guilty. If making peace is not possible, then Frankl suggests finding some means to express the guilt. For example, one might find a way of offering recompense for harm that has been done in the past or do something good for the person towards whom there is a moral debt. When there is no capacity to do any of these things, he says, one can at least deeply and truthfully live through what has happened, take the blame upon oneself, and by doing so become a different person.

On this point, Vladika Anthony told the following story. An elderly woman once told him that she was plagued by nightmares from her past. She could not forget what she had done, and in her dreams this event continuously came back to her. She did not know what to do about it. Vladika gave her this advice: She should put herself back in the situation as it happened, and then honestly and courageously ask herself, "If I were to find myself in exactly the same situation with all of my present experience of life, would I behave in the same way or not?" Vladika told her that if she could truthfully say that in no way, under no circumstances, would she do the same thing again, then she had become a new person – it was not the old her anymore. The past no longer had any relationship with the person she was now. The feeling of guilt would then disappear, since it no longer had anything in common with her. However, if she felt she would act in the very same way as she had done in the past, then this was a problem of the present, something she must struggle with now.

As I experience it, a feeling of guilt is unproductive as long as one does not look at the root cause and this requires working on oneself. Often the feeling of guilt is closely related to forgiveness; forgiveness not only of the other person but of oneself as well. If I can accept myself as I am, even with my moral ugliness, I will have the strength to go further, to carry the weight of my own faults and failures in the past. If feelings of guilt are processed in this active way, we can learn to act differently and reconciliation can result.

In regard to the feeling of guilt prior to death, I can quote Vladika Anthony:

It is extremely necessary to prepare for one's death by a severe but freeing process of reconciliation with everyone: with oneself, one's conscience, one's circumstances, with the present and the past, with events... also in relation to people, and even with the future and the coming of death itself. It is impossible to enter eternity when one is entangled in hatred, in a state of unrest. Both the dying person and the ones still left behind on earth need to be able to say from the depth of their heart: "Forgive me," and then, "I do forgive you."[15]

Man's Indomitable Spirit

Etty Hillesum, the young Dutch Jewish woman mentioned earlier, is for me one of the most moving examples of a spirit which could not be broken.

At the age of twenty-nine she was transported to a concentration camp where she wrote the following words in her diary, knowing she would soon die in the gas chambers: "I am suffering to the limit of what one can suffer. However, I do not cling to my suffering; it is going through me as life itself, as a broad, eternal river... life goes on."[16] Viktor Frankl, too, learned from his time in the camps that man had enormous resources and could survive even the most terrible situations.

The same point is brought home by a situation in our hospice:

Sophie was twelve years old. She and her mother were very close and both extremely alive. The mother's positive energy spilled over to her daughter, and it seemed to me that this was why Sophie had lived much longer than the medical professionals

15 *Antonij mitr. Surozhskij*, "Zhizn'. Bolezn'. Smert'.: Smert'." Moskva: Fond Duhovnoe nasledie Mitropolita Antoniya Surozhskogo, 2010 (Russian) [*Metropolitan Anthony of Sourozh*, "Life. Illness. Death: On Death." Moscow: Metropolitan Anthony of Sourozh Spiritual Foundation, 2010]

16 Etty Hillesum. *Une vie bouleversée: journal 1941-1943: suivi de lettres de Westerbork [An Interrupted Life: The Diaries 1941-1943, and Letters from Westerbork]*, trad. de nederl. par P. Noble, (Paris: Ed. de Seuil,1991).

expected. Many times, she had been on the brink of death and had even come out of deep coma to talk again. I felt intense joy at once more hearing her lovely voice after a long period of silence.

It seemed to me that Sophie continued to fight for her life for her mother's sake, and although her chemotherapy continued, the illness progressed until she became paralyzed. She suffered a great deal and her strength dwindled, yet what amazed me was the expression of her bright blue eyes. In spite of everything, they expressed such a depth of life and mischief that I thought I had never before seen such a lively spirit, a spirit that could not be quenched by anything.

As she reclined in a wheelchair shortly before her death, she had a sense of humor that did not leave her. Her eyes, with their unfathomable depths, never stopped shining. When Sophie's life eventually came to an end, it was clear to me that she could not really die and that she was now totally alive in God. During her short life, it was precisely God's own strength that had given her such an indomitable spirit.

CHAPTER THREE

Different Stages in Accepting an Existential Crisis

The Swiss-American psychiatrist Elisabeth Kübler-Ross[17] had a deep knowledge of such crises, based on her long experience of people's reactions to living through trauma and loss, including the prospect of their own death. Each of the people she observed had tackled an existential crisis and had come face to face with death in all of its different forms: disease, suicide, road accidents, and so on.

In her book *On Death and Dying*, Kübler-Ross talks about the different stages of loss that a person goes through when suddenly faced with a serious crisis, particularly death and dying. She mentions five stages, which do not necessarily occur in straight chronological order: denial, anger, bargaining, depression, and acceptance.

I will discuss these stages from my own experience with patients in our hospice.

Stage One - Denial

Often this is the first reaction to a serious crisis. People may cry out: "This is a mistake, it is not me, it cannot be." Kübler-Ross was of the opinion that denial can serve as a kind of defense mechanism. It is a desperate effort to come to terms with what is happening in the first phase of an agonizing situation. At this stage, the patient and his relatives often blame the doctors, the nurses, the treatment,

17 Elisabeth Kübler-Ross (1926-2004) was a Swiss-American psychiatrist, a pioneer in near-death studies and the author of the groundbreaking book *On Death and Dying* (Routledge: 1969), where she first discussed her theory of the five stages of grief, also known as the "Kübler-Ross model".

or complain that there is a mistaken case history, a wrong diagnosis, a bad hospital. It is important to understand that these outbursts of anger, reproach, and complaint are not really directed at the medical profession. They are an expression of emotional turmoil, shock, fear, and despair.

Stage Two – Anger

Often, in my experience, anger is the result of a sudden awareness of loss of control over one's life and body. It can also be an expression of unbearable pain, emotional and physical. It is always worth remembering that the person diagnosed with a serious or terminal illness suddenly loses almost everything: status in society, the ability to work and be financially independent, and perhaps even social contacts and friends. (When a calamity occurs, one comes to know one's real friends and may well lose some.)

This person forfeits independence and will often fear becoming a burden to others.

Among the hardest things to accept is the prospect of no longer being active in any of the ways that we usually take for granted. On a sexual level, illness reduces the patient's capacity to be physically intimate with a partner. Perhaps for the first time, the person will be intensely conscious of the body as something more than an outer shell, as something that is his or her real self. So, what happens to this body becomes very important.

I have noticed that especially for women their outer appearance, how they look, becomes a real issue. For instance, after a mastectomy many women feel that they have lost their femininity. The loss of hair and having to wear a wig can also be hard to take. I also remember a beautiful young woman with widespread melanoma (skin cancer) which had spread all over the lower part of her body. During the doctor's round, it was clear that she was ashamed of showing anyone her body from the way she hastily pulled the sheet over herself.

It is at this stage that there will often be anger, irritation, and impatience: "Nothing is good enough," the patient will seem to say in a very demanding way. According to Kübler-Ross this is an expression of the soul crying out: "I am still alive, do not forget that! I have not died yet!"

Vladika Anthony said that anger can be a good and real sign of life, adding that anger can also stand for deep pain which cannot be expressed otherwise.

It is tragic that we (as caregivers) often respond to anger as though it was directed at ourselves. We take it personally rather than trying to understand what it stands for, what the real reason is for these bouts of bad temper and irritation. More often than not, at this stage of the patient's experience of loss, angry outbursts have nothing to do with those of us who are on the receiving end.

As an illustration, in our hospice was a still-young artist called Nina, who continued to paint until the end of her life. She placed heavy demands on all those people around her, but behind this smokescreen of demands stood a small person crying out to be cherished. It seemed to me that, perhaps unknowingly, she was testing us: "Will you still accept me if I behave in an awful way?" Not long before her death she openly expressed the wish to die at our hospice and nowhere else. Having probed us, she had accepted us.

When a person becomes terminally ill with cancer, he or she loses everything that has hitherto been familiar. Often there is little time to adjust to this painful change of circumstances and status.

When I look at a patient who has recently become bedridden, it becomes painfully clear that it is now of very little importance whether this person has been a scholar or a simple workman. It no longer matters whether the person was intelligent or otherwise, whether he was rich or poor. All that remains is a bedside table, perhaps a vase with some flowers, a glass of water. The only difference that matters is between people's reaction to their illness and mortality.

To accept the fact that one is dying and to take responsibility for the way one relates to this is very difficult – much harder than being angry, irritable, and dissatisfied with everything and everyone. To my mind, the supreme challenge of finding meaning in one's suffering is the key to living courageously through this stage.

If a patient finds it impossible to accept his or her condition, it is often far from easy for the relatives, the medical personnel and psychotherapists to deal with the resulting anger. If the patient (and sometimes the relatives as well) get stuck in this stage of anger, this is often a sign that they are trapped in a stance of victimhood and refusing to take responsibility for facing reality with the right cast of mind.

As we have seen, for those without an inner support system, an inner "crutch," it will be very difficult indeed to let go of these fears and inner protests. I have more than once heard a patient saying: "But I have always been a good person, why me?" I think it can be useful to talk this over with the person. It can be helpful to recall gently that he or she is not the only one who is facing the prospect of death, that this fate is common to all of us. One can also talk about the calling we all have to live up to our potential for human greatness, to be an example to others, and to show that it is possible to live in a dignified way right to the end.

However, in this cry of "Why me?" or "I have always been a good person," there may be the unconscious feeling that God is delivering a punishment. Or there may be an expression of guilt. At such times, when the patient reports a feeling of receiving retribution from God, I say that I myself do not know or believe in a God who punishes His people. I suggest that perhaps there is another way to look at this illness. One can even discuss with the patient the possibility that, at times, illness is the only thing that will make a person stop, look, and evaluate how he has been living.

It is my belief that the state of our soul, which will continue to live after we die, is more important to God than the state of our present physical body. According to Vladika Anthony, God sometimes allows us to fall ill in order to stop us from being prisoners of the things that bind us too firmly to our earthly existence, the things that prevent us from living life to the full in communion with God.

When illness strikes, we should look at ourselves and take full responsibility for the way we have been relating to ourselves (including our bodies), to God, to people, and to life in general. There are laws in nature that have to be respected. So often, in my experience, illnesses are a result of how we have lived our inner life, which may be nurturing feelings of resentment, hatred, greed, fears, jealousy. All of our negative feelings and thoughts have their repercussions on our body, on our state of health. Of course, ecology and heredity also play a role in illness, but so do unhealthy eating habits, smoking, drinking, and lack of exercise. A simple absence of joy and an excess of stress over a long period of time are also prime causes: at some point the body cannot take it any longer and just succumbs.

Here is an example:

I vividly remember a sixty-year-old patient, a simple, uneducated person, called John. He was suffering from cancer of the throat and a tracheostomy had been put in place that made it difficult to speak clearly. Not long before he died, he said to me unexpectedly, "I have lived badly; I will not be saved." Right up to now, I have this picture in front of me: John is sitting on his bed, a terrible smell is coming from his oozing tracheostomy site, and he is looking at me with sad eyes full of trust. In answer to his cry of despair (knowing a little about Russian reality) I asked him: "Did you drink?" He nodded. "Did you steal?" "Yes." "Did you beat anyone?" Again, he nodded. Then he sat silently. He did not justify himself in any way. He had simply looked at his life and at himself truthfully and said to himself: "Yes. I have lived badly." To me, it seemed that he had shown such honesty and courage in taking responsibility for his life and illness that he would be given peace after his death.

Stage Three – Bargaining

Bargaining, in essence, is trying to influence one's destiny and to postpone the inevitable. This stage normally does not last long, but sometimes while in it the terminally ill person makes a promise to fate or to God. For example: "I will cycle around the world, collect a lot of money and give it to a worthy cause"; "If I am healed, I will live in a new and better way"; or it may be that he promises to give his organs to science when he dies, if only he can get better now. From a psychological point of view, this wish to give something in exchange for healing may point to a sense of guilt.

In order to support someone at this stage and to help him or her not to get stuck there, it is necessary to stay close by and let the person talk. The caregiver must accept him, where he is at, and who he is at every moment. Then, perhaps, the patient will understand that this sort of bargaining is not a real solution to the problem.

Stage Four – Depression

Depression is a natural reaction to a person's understanding that the changed life situation is real and unavoidable. Kübler-Ross talked about two types of depression. The first is a response to what is happening – reactionary depression. As we have already discussed, a terminally ill patient loses almost everything that he is used to. In addition to this, deep anxieties can surface at this stage including fear of separation and loss, fear of becoming a burden, fear of unbearable pain, and fear of the unknown.

The second type of depression appears when the person is preparing for death, for an imminent transition into the other world. At this stage, paradoxically, the patient is not in need of a large number of eager visitors, nor does the sick person require false cheering up or an excess of chatter. More than ever, he or she is in need of our silent presence. At this stage, according to Kübler-Ross, one has to let the patient express sorrow and there should be no attempt to suppress this feeling. Allowing sorrow to be articulated is a step toward enabling the patient to acquire some badly needed inner peace.

Here, I quote Vladika Anthony:

> It is necessary for a person that we are with him in his sorrow, at the depth of his grief, and he does not need to be told that he has no right to grieve. We should give time to let grace and the inner experience a person has acquired do its work. There is no need to

comfort a person with empty words. The most important thing is to be there and to be silent. While being with a patient, we must be so silent and so open that at any moment, he can start talking to us.[18]

It is at this stage of preparation for death that the patient may have less need of relatives. I think that it is important to explain to the relatives that this is not a rejection of them but a sign that the person is now very courageously, step by step, entering a realm where they cannot yet follow. If this matter is not discussed, it may well be that for the rest of his or her life, a spouse may mistakenly live with the feeling of having been rejected at the end of the couple's life together. The bereaved spouse is left with bitterness instead of realizing that this phase is part of the patient's preparation to enter a new world.

Depression is often a natural and necessary step along the way to accepting death. It is the beginning of going through sorrow and loss. However, one frequently notices a discrepancy between the moods and expectations of the patient and those of the relatives. Situations can arise where the patient is prepared and ready for the "long journey," but the relatives are not yet ready to let go. With all their might, they still try to give their loved one (and more so, themselves) a false hope that "everything will be fine" and that recovery is still possible.

18 Antonij mitr. Surozhskij, "Zhizn'. Bolezn'. Smert'.: Pastyr' u posteli bol'nogo." Moskva: Fond Duhovnoe nasledie Mitropolita Antoniya Surozhskogo, 2010 (Russian) [Metropolitan Anthony of Sourozh, "Life. Illness. Death: Pastoral Care of the Sick and Dying." Moscow: Metropolitan Anthony of Sourozh Spiritual Foundation, 2010] Talks with Fr. Sergei Hackel for BBC Russian religious program "Resurrection," October, 1993 - January, 1994, London.

Stage Five – Acceptance

Kübler-Ross does not view this as a joyful stage. As she sees it, this is when all feelings and strength are leaving the patient. The pain may have gone and this is the moment where the person, metaphorically or literally, takes a last deep breath before what she calls "the long journey."

With the patients I have known, I experienced this stage differently. To me it does not seem that all feelings and strength have disappeared. It may be that the very opposite is happening. At times, one notices a fine-tuning of the patient's senses. Unexpectedly, the patient may look up in amazement, clearly seeing or communicating with someone or something who is invisible to us.

This happens fairly frequently, usually following a definite period of struggle, after which the patient can be given a deep sense of peace. At this point, one senses an almost tangible stillness, which to me is an indication that the fight has been fought and death is close. It is a visible turning point in the patient's preparation for entry into the other world.

There are, of course, exceptions. There are also patients who fight to the bitter end, hoping against hope that they are not going to die. This, I feel, prevents them from finally reaching stillness and peace within themselves.

At this point, relatives may have to reduce the number of visitors and simply remain with the person who is dying, in stillness and in harmony with him. Later, we will discuss the support which should be given to the relatives themselves, since they and the patient should be seen as a single reality.

Here, I want to mention that the relatives may be facing not only the death of their loved one, but the reality of death in general. This may be the first time in their lives that they have come face-to-face with the fact that they also will die one day.

Here is an example of how the stages mentioned above do not always come in a logical or chronological order:

Seventeen-year-old Ilya was admitted to our hospice twice. When he was first admitted I asked him what he knew about his illness and how he understood his prognosis. He looked at me and answered simply, "I know that I will die soon." "What does that mean to you?" I asked, and the teenager replied: "You know, I have learned to live every day to the full." Then, after a short while, he added: "But I will not die... how can I leave my mother? How will she manage without me?"

In this case, Ilya's mother was an uneducated person with the inborn courage and ability to take life as it comes, however painful and incomprehensible. Her courage allowed her son to face his own death. His changeable attitude, however, is a clear example of how the stages of facing one's death can alternate with one another. A person seems at first to have accepted death, but then denies that it is actually happening. Reality may be too painful to contemplate steadily all of the time. However, the basic fact remains that once death has been accepted, one can live to the full and enjoy each day.

Upon his second admission to the hospice it was clear that Ilya had little time left. Somehow, he knew that he would die in a few days and, without stating why, asked his mother to take three days off of work. Two days later he lost his eyesight, and on the third day he peacefully and calmly died in his mother's presence.

Meaning and hope also factor into the timing of one's death. It was Frankl's experience in the concentration camps that as soon as an inmate gave up hope, he would die within days. He talks about how closely the state of a man's soul and his immune system are interrelated. He knows how fatal it can be when one loses hope and the will to live. He gives an example of a friend in the camp whose bitter disappointment caused him to lose his hope and longing for the future. As a result, his body succumbed to illness; his immune system could not fight any longer.

In England, I heard the following story: A priest's wife had been diagnosed with advanced breast cancer and her doctors had given her only four months to live. However, it was her burning wish to live at least until her seven-year-old daughter reached the age of fourteen. This in fact happened, and I think it was because of her strong faith and deep hope. Another factor, perhaps, was that she had a very particular aim to live for.

The opposite happened in the following case:

> Michael, a fifty-year-old patient in an English hospice, was eagerly waiting for his wife to take him home, but that very morning he was told that she had refused to come for him. He listened to this without saying a word, then he turned to the wall. The very next day he died. I remember him to this day because, to my mind, there is nothing worse than realizing that the person you love and trust most does not want anything to do with you at the very moment you are seriously ill and standing before death.

Kübler-Ross was also of the opinion that one should not take hope away from the dying. There are many cases where patients (along with their relatives) seem to have accepted that death is imminent, but shortly before the end they express the hope that there will be a last-minute cure. Kübler-Ross thought that such ideas should not be contradicted, but I feel that the issue of giving hope to a dying patient is a complex one.

Somehow, one has to tell the truth and yet not take away all hope. One should certainly not follow the example of some relatives, who right until the end proclaim with false cheerfulness that everything is going to be fine, "You are getting better and better." In my view, it is important to talk openly with the relatives and the patient who, in any case, knows from the state of his body that death is approaching. One could also follow the advice given by Metropolitan Anthony and say, "Yes, like all of us, you are going to die, but not yet. We are all under God's protection...."

Or if it is appropriate, I sometimes say, "Yes, from a medical view, things are not so good, but there is always the possibility of a sudden change or a miracle." One should not underestimate how much positive influence can be exercised by a doctor, nurse, or relative. It will help enormously if this caregiver can convey to the patient (preferably without words) their faith that death is not the end. Then, the caregiver becomes a reassuring presence, conveying the message that there is nothing to fear and that the patient will not be left alone.

CHAPTER FOUR

Communicating with Seriously Ill Patients

The Uniqueness of Each Person

In the first encounter with a patient, one has to take into account this person's previous encounters with illness and the burdens of his or her life. Every human being carries around a vast body of experience, both positive and negative. When a patient has had negative experiences in the field of medicine this can affect all subsequent relationships with medical professionals.

One kind of negative experience that can impact the patient has to do with the manner and behavior shown by doctors. If, during previous encounters, the doctors seemed only to be interested in symptoms that showed up on the computer, this will have left a lasting effect. If the practitioner did not seem to have any concern for the patient as a person, that also may have caused the patient to close up and lose faith in the medical world. The patient understandably feels that he has not been regarded as an individual in his own right; he has therefore not been examined properly as a human being or listened to.

Each person comes with a particular past and present, with a particular set of feelings and fears, with particular experiences of family, education, and career. Each person has a longing to be seen in depth, not superficially, but as a unique human being with a distinct character, with good and bad traits. People yearn to be seen as a unique creation, on whose soul God has left His eternal stamp.

A patient may have a backlog of anxieties rooted in previous encounters with illness, treatment, and with the death of relatives or close friends. One also has to take into account that nowadays most patients will have researched their symptoms and diagnosis on the computer and are already anticipating the very worst. All of this will deeply influence a patient's attitude towards his or her illness and prognosis. It can also affect the state of mind and soul. There may be deep fear or depression based on the anticipation of what, in the patient's imagination, lies ahead. If the patient seems obstinate about refusing to comply with the prescribed treatment, it is worth trying to find out the reason why.

More than anything, a seriously ill patient needs to be surrounded by people who are not anxious but quiet and calm, without the excessive talking that can exhaust him. The ill person needs all the attention possible, but without the kind of "fussing" that too often expresses the relatives' own fear and anxiety. It frequently happens that visitors come and stay much too long; they do not notice that the patient is getting exhausted and the patient does not want to cause offence by asking the well-wishers to leave.

It is better not to admit too many people at once into the presence of a very ill patient. It is preferable that they come, at most, in pairs, rather than crowding round or towering over the sick person. Larger groups can be too much for the patient to take in, and they also reduce the amount of oxygen in the room, which is the last thing that a person with breathing problems needs.

When we visit a patient, we should remember that it is the quality rather than the length of the meeting that matters. Ideally, each person who receives a visit should feel that they have been seen and heard as a human being who is unique, important, and needed.

In order to have a real meeting of this kind with a sick person, one has to learn to let go of unnecessary emotions, thoughts, words, and bodily movements. Try to be totally still, simply to "be" with an open heart. Learning to do this is not easy.

Instead of talking, one should aim to be silent, simply being with the patient and waiting for what will come. One should not spend time planning in advance what to say or what to do, which can be a defense mechanism. Rather, one should convey a quiet understanding that what will happen, will happen; that is enough.

I am convinced that this is the only way for relatives, doctors and nurses to gain a real ability to see and hear the patient. Achieving this requires the discipline of learning to be totally present in each moment of time. It involves learning to be in the "here and now," without any thoughts, feelings, and worries (for example, about what to say). This requires a willingness to let go of oneself, one's ego. It is not "me" who is the center but the person in front of me.

Moreover, if one wants to learn to be present in this way, then it has to be a matter of the heart. We must train our hearts to respond with deep compassion to each person in need, whether we happen to like the person or not. This person has a right to be the way he or she is, however different that might be from our own way of being.

Here I would like to quote Vladika Anthony on the education of the heart:

> If we want to educate our heart, what stands in the way most of all is our fear in the face of suffering, emotional pain, and spiritual tragedy. We are afraid of suffering and this is why we make our hearts narrow, why we defend ourselves. We are afraid to look and see, we are afraid to listen and hear, we are afraid to see a person suffering and to hear the cry from his soul. This is why we close up. And by closing up, we become narrower and narrower until we become prisoners of our own shut-down being.[19]

Vladika then gives the following illustration:

> In order to protect themselves from peril, the most fragile sea creatures build around themselves a hard wall of matter which we call corals, and inside this protective wall they are dying. The same thing happens to a person who protects himself against pain and suffering, against the fear and terror of what another's sorrow, another's illness, another's death will do to him…he protects himself against all of the horrors of life on earth. Yes, he will be protected, but in such an internal state he is dying….

19 Antonij mitr. Surozhskij, "Chelovek pered Bogom: Vospitanie serdca, a ne trenirovka voli": iz gl. 3 Put' podviga. Moskva: Fond Duhovnoe nasledie mitropolita Antoniya Surozhskogo, 2010 (Russian). [Metropolitan Anthony of Sourozh, *Man Before God: The Way of Discipline*, Ch. 3: "The Education of the Heart, Not the Training of the Will," Moscow: Metropolitan Anthony of Sourozh Spiritual Foundation, 2010].

If a person wants to educate his heart in order to make it alive, he needs to put a very direct question to himself, "Am I ready to take into my heart any suffering, of whatever kind? Am I ready to have compassion for each person who is ill, who is terrified, who is cold, who is hungry, who has been wounded by life in whatever way?"[20]

Compassion

The concept of compassion is closely related to the concept of the uniqueness of each individual. Once we fully understand that no two people are alike, this will prompt us to treat each patient, whoever they may be, with great respect.

It is important to understand that compassion is *not* an expression of one's emotions. Vladika Anthony talks about the necessity to have compassion in a creative way:

We need to train ourselves in such a way that we will be able to respond with all our mind, all our heart – but without attempting (almost physically from within) to force ourselves to feel suffering that is not ours or emotions that do not belong to us. The patient has no need of our living through his pain; he is in need of our creative response to his suffering and his condition. He is in need of a creative response of the sort that will move us to action, one which is rooted in respect and in reverence towards him – a person who has a name, specific facial features, a wife or husband or a beloved one, or who has a child and is of a particular age. This person, whether I like him or not, is important. The worth of each person is expressed in the totality of the life and death of Christ.[21]

20 Ibid.

21 Antonij mitr. Surozhskij, "Chelovecheskie cennosti v medicine," Trudy: v 2-h kn. Kn. 1, iz gl. Materiya i Duh. Moskva: Praktika, 2002, 27 p. (Russian) [Metropolitan Anthony of Sourozh Human Values in Medicine. Talk delivered to the Bristol Medico-Chirurgical Society on May 8, 1974. *Bristol Medico-Chirurgical Journal*, Vol. 91, 1976. (http://masar-chive.org/Sites/texts/1974-05-08-1-E-R-T-EM05-37HumanValuesInMedicine.html)

In order to be compassionate, one has to learn to be sober and collected. It is the dying patient who should be in the center, not our own emotions and feeling. This needs to be remembered by doctors and nurses but to an even greater extent by the patient's relatives and friends. The patient has enough of his own pain and fear to cope with. When the people around him are crying and agitated, this only makes the patient's own struggle more intense and may make him feel guilty.

It is well known that for caregivers dealing with a seriously ill patient, it is equally important to look after that person's relatives, as together they form one closely connected whole. The emotional state of a relative inevitably spills over onto the patient himself and has a deep effect. This, in turn, impacts the whole range of symptoms: physical, emotional and spiritual.

This is why, for those looking after someone who is gravely ill, a certain discipline and sobriety is needed so that the sadness and despair of other people will not be transmitted to the patient. Whenever medical personnel find themselves emotionally involved in the story of a patient, I feel that it is better for them to postpone the expression of their sadness and grief to a later stage. It can be expressed at home perhaps, away from the patient and relatives.

This is not a question of showing a stiff upper lip. Without being dramatic, it is possible and necessary for a caregiver to express sorrow over the patient's suffering and imminent death, and there are ways to let the patient know that he or she is loved. This can be demonstrated not by overt displays of emotion but, for example, by being willing to stay with the patient as long as is necessary, through direct eye contact, or by touching the patient with tenderness.

As already noted, compassion is rooted more than anything else in silence, in the ability to be still. If we can sit with the patient quietly, without any defenses or fears, this will have a deep effect. Without the need for words, it will assure the patient that we are not afraid to stay close, whatever happens, right to the very end. This will also create a deep relationship of trust, which allows the patient to talk about whatever is troubling him or her the most.

Sometimes I ask a patient: "If you want to, tell me please what it means to you to be unable to control your illness? Can you help me understand what you are going through? If you agree, this will not only be of great benefit to me but also to other patients who are in the same position."

I ask this for different reasons. First of all, the patient will understand that we respect him and relate to him as a person who is needed. Secondly, the patient will have the feeling of being able to give something to others despite being terminally ill. This, in a small way, can give some meaning to suffering. Kübler-Ross said that if a patient can give something of himself to others and thus express his personality, he will not so easily become prone to depression.

When a patient becomes aware of the ability to help others who are suffering similar trials, including imminent death, this can be a way of avoiding the trap of all-engulfing self-pity.

How to Inform a Patient of His Diagnosis

Vladika Anthony once said that you cannot light-heartedly tell a person that "you are going to die," as long as the patient has a deep fear of death. In this case, Vladika said, it is important to try to help the patient discover what life in eternity actually means. One should try to ascertain to what extent the sick person already, from experience, has some sense of this. Because when there is no doubt that life after death will continue, this will help him to overcome and let go of the fear of death. This does not imply ignoring the pain of separation, or ceasing to feel bitterness over the simple fact that mortality exists. But fear of death, as such, will disappear.

One should not define life eternal from a time-based point of view as an experience of never-ending duration, but rather in terms of the quality of a life which is "brimming over its edge."

Eternal life, for Vladika Anthony, does not mean living forever without any end, which in itself may be a far from pleasant prospect. On the contrary, it refers to a fullness of life; it means to be so alive as to have a sense that this cannot be taken away under any circumstances. He quotes St. John the Evangelist in stating that eternity is not something but Someone: God and the fullness of His being with whom we will commune.

In this connection, I remember something that happened many years ago when I worked in a London hospital where we were not allowed to talk about death:

A middle-aged man who had been a dancer all his life had been admitted to our ward. As his death grew closer, he unexpectedly asked me straight out: "Do you think that I will kick the bucket?" I pretended not to understand what he was referring to, although I knew full well what he meant. After this, I felt ashamed of myself. The following day he looked at me, and in the presence of some relatives, he asked, "Do you think that 'over there' I will be able to dance?" This time, I was able to say "Yes" to him with all my being and assure him that he would certainly be dancing again. His relatives looked at me in astonishment: "But he is not even able to walk!" With a broad smile the patient kept looking at me. He had seen that this time I had not avoided his question.

When patients (especially younger ones) are told their diagnosis, they often go straight to the internet to find out about the horrific symptoms and treatments they are sure they will encounter. The fear of these horrors will continue to haunt them, so it is necessary to enquire about this in particular when you meet patients who are overwhelmed with fear.

Here is another instance:

Alexandra was sixteen years old. On admission in the hospice, she was in a deep depression, almost in a stupor. She had been diagnosed with cancer of the breast, already in an advanced stage. On the internet, she had read about the terrible pain that lay ahead. Moreover, she had read that with metastasis the pain would be so severe that it would almost be impossible to alleviate it.

This is actually not true, but Alexandra was already living totally in this terrifying future although her physical condition upon admission was not so bad. She felt that all hope was gone and, as we have already discussed, when there is no hope the body succumbs and gives up fighting. She fell into such a deep depression that she could hardly speak. It took a long time before she slowly began to communicate and had even a slight interest in doing something herself. She started to read a little and to knit a scarf, although without much enthusiasm.

What had made matters worse was that her mother refused to be with her in the "here and now." She too already lived in the future because it was apparently too painful to share her daughter's agony. So, in her mind she already had her daughter buried. All she talked about was how she could possibly cope without her after the funeral. The fact that her daughter was still alive and in great need of warmth and support seemed to pass her by. As a result, Alexandra was left on her own to cope with her fears and depression.

Gradually she came out of her depression, not totally, but at least she showed some interest in the things going on around her and she was no longer overwhelmed by her fears. But there were still some tough moments. Shortly before she died, I saw her sitting alone on her bed. She seemed so tiny and utterly vulnerable, perched there helplessly like a little bird with ruffled feathers.

This is an example of how fear can keep a patient in its grip. This can happen when there is too much information, and information not always relevant to the person's illness and particular condition. A negative picture of the future will be created in the patient's mind, making it impossible to deal with the reality of the immediate situation. This can often lead to despair, to a complete loss of hope which diminishes the patient's physical resistance towards his illness and hastens death.

When there is an acute crisis or a patient is dying, you often hear the question: "What is going to happen?!" However, if a patient seems to be asking, "Am I dying?" this does not always indicate a desire for a real answer, for the truth.

In order to find out if the patient really feels ready to discuss the situation, I sometimes ask, "Forgive me, I have somehow forgotten your diagnosis, could you please remind me?" The answer may be clear: "I have cancer," often followed by a pause. Alternatively, one may hear something like, "I do not know, no one has told me." In that case, one can continue by asking about the treatments the patient has had. Has there been any chemotherapy or radiation, and in what type of hospital has he been? At times, if a patient denies all knowledge of the diagnosis, I just change the subject to something totally different. At that point, the patient may unexpectedly and very quickly add, "But I have cancer of the lungs..." before continuing to talk about something else; that is, anything rather than what he has just revealed.

This is an indication that the patient is not quite ready to discuss the diagnosis but, nevertheless, wants me to know. In general, it takes a great deal of careful listening to find out whether a patient is ready to discuss the fact that death is imminent. Therefore, it is very important to have a picture of the patient's character and circumstances: to know whether there is support at home, and what the work situation is. One must know something about the patient's attitude to life, beliefs, level of courage, and ability to tolerate negativity and conflict. Learning to read the patient's body language can also be an invaluable way of knowing what he or she really wants or is trying to say.

If a relationship of trust has been built up from the beginning, this will help. It may be that a patient chooses to trust one particular person with whom it is possible to openly discuss the prognosis, and in whose presence it can be accepted that life will not continue much longer.

In this case, the trusted individual should stay with the patient, silently listening and never giving the impression of being in a hurry. He or she should only leave the patient after feeling satisfied that the worst of the sick person's anxieties, fears, and feelings of anger have eased and given way to at least some sense of peace.

I remember an episode from my own life in London. Once, after a talk by Vladika Anthony, I was standing in church when a great sense of unrest and anxiety suddenly overcame me. I wanted to leave, but somehow the bishop intuitively picked up my feelings and said to me: "Come and sit down." Then he began talking to me about something that I do not remember, some small talk, which for him was rather unusual. Then after a little while, he got up, said goodbye and left.

It was only much later that I realized what he had done. He had felt my anxiety and sat me down to talk in order to allay this unrest. He had not mentioned anything specific, but it was only when he felt that peace had returned that he left me, without explaining anything. (I dare say he also prayed while talking to me.)

To me, this was a lesson for life. It taught me simply to stay, whenever possible, alongside anyone in whom I sense turmoil, whether or not they are patients of mine. Even a smile or a short, silent prayer will help when one comes across someone in this agitated state.

In cases when a patient appears restless or sad, I sometimes sit down and talk about something else, not mentioning the signs of anxiety. Then I may ask the sick person to recall an exceptionally beautiful and happy experience in his life. In this way, I try to help the patient relive something joyful and full of light. Instead of dwelling on the dark and negative, I encourage the patient to realize that life has been worth living, that it has not passed by in vain. This, I feel, acts as a kind of support and reduces the risk of depression.

As we have seen, a patient is not always ready to discuss the imminence of death. However, if the sick person persists in denial, this can mean that they will have to face mortality alone.

Or perhaps the patient does somehow know that death is coming but because of fear or the attitude of relatives, does not dare to come face to face with this hard fact:

In the hospice was a middle-aged patient, Olga, with her husband John. As I entered her room for the first time, Olga's husband stopped me and sternly said that Olga did not know her diagnosis and that under no circumstances should she be told.

We went in together and he began to forcefully feed his wife. She did not want to eat at all and began crying. John shouted at her, insisting that there was no reason to cry. I could only remain silent, standing on the other side of the bed.

Olga then turned away from her husband and looked at me with dark eyes full of tears. All I could say, keeping eye contact, was, "Sometimes things are so painful that one can only cry, isn't that right, Olga?" Without a word she nodded; she saw that someone had understood her.

She died the following day. Her husband John became hysterical. He now felt guilty that he had never been truthful to Olga. He had to face everything at once: his guilt, despair, and hidden fears, in addition to his grief at having lost his wife. The two of them had gone through pain and the fear of death in total isolation, unable to support each other and to live through this sorrow together. Nor had there been any way to resolve practical or financial questions.

Communicating with Words

In human communication, a mere seven percent of information is expressed by words alone. The rest is indicated by the tone of voice, the expression of the eyes, gestures, body language, and other nonverbal expressions. Things are also conveyed by silence and, above all, by the matters about which a person does not speak. Also, serious illness often leads to a heightened sensitivity to what is going on in the immediate surroundings. The patient can read nonverbal expressions with great accuracy.

This is one reason why it is so necessary for those who are dealing with such patients to work on themselves first. They should have worked through their own fears and defenses and let them go. They should have acquired the ability to be silent in order to perceive the patient's deep needs and unspoken cries from the soul.

In her book, *How to Be a Friend to a Friend Who's Sick*, Letty Cottin Pogrebin speaks from her own experience of having been a patient. She observes that when one is very ill, one wants to reduce the number of visitors.

I have also seen many relatives and visitors crowding around a patient who is dying. They rarely realize that their own sorrow, their feelings of inadequacy, their fears of death, are having a direct, negative influence on the patient. Often, they engage in endless chatter to cover up their feelings of inadequacy and ignorance of how to behave or what to say.

As is noted by Pogrebin, the patient can read a lot into the tone of the simple question, "How are you?" From the way this question is asked, the patient can sense the anxiety and fears felt by the relatives and friends who have gathered at the bedside. Pogrebin's advice is that one should ask a different question: "What are you feeling?" She adds that when you dishonestly tell a patient "You look wonderful," the sick person will immediately sense from the intonation that the opposite is true. This dishonesty will result in a lack of trust, and the patient will be left alone to face the coming travail. Pogrebin has much more advice for visitors on how they can improve their communication with patients who are seriously ill.[22]

These points are relevant not only for concerned relatives or loved ones but also for medical staff, volunteers, priests, and anyone else looking after the terminally ill. We have already discussed the importance of working on oneself when dealing with such patients: I must learn to forget about myself, accepting that the patient is in the center, not me. I have to let go of personal defense mechanisms in order to see, hear, and understand the patient in depth.

If we want to look at some "rules" for better communication, in my experience there is one thing that we should contemplate first and foremost, and that is silence. The discipline of silence is of the greatest importance when dealing with people. This silence entails not only the absence of words, but a silencing of superfluous thoughts, emotions, and of bodily movement. All of this is necessary to be one hundred percent present in the "here and now," to be able to listen and hear, to watch and see what is really happening with the patient. Each person we meet should

---

22 Letti Kottin Pogrebin, Ispytanie bolezn'yu. (Moskva: Live Book, 2014.) p 99. [Letty Kottin Pogrebin, *How to Be a Friend to a Friend Who's Sick.* (Moscow: Live Book, 2014) p. 99.].

feel that we are completely present and that nothing will break our communication even if there are many other patients and tasks awaiting us.

Vladika Anthony once told me that if you look at your watch when speaking to someone, then you can be sure that the whole conversation has been in vain. The person you are speaking with will have an acute feeling of being of no importance, and any newly built-up trust will be broken. I strongly feel that this point has become even more relevant in today's world with our endless use of mobile phones. It seems to have become the norm that any call, at any time, has to be answered immediately, regardless of the conversation we are having.

It is not the length of our meeting or conversation that matters but its quality and depth. A person who is treated as being of unique importance, the only one who matters, will come away feeling that he or she has been seen, even if the meeting is short.

At the end of such a meeting, it is possible to say to the sick person: "Thank you, it was so good that we met. Now I have to see to the other patients, but I will come and see you again at the end of the day." This promise, of course, has to be kept so as not to break the trust that has developed.

Closely connected to this is the problem of the "difficult" patient who keeps calling the nurses. This we have seen, is also a kind of cry: "Please do notice me, I am not dead yet, I am "I". It expresses the unspoken plea: "Do not leave me, spend time with me, I feel so frightened. I am so out of control...." When one takes time to be totally present, this individual will become quieter and far less demanding. This is because he knows that at least for one person he is important as a fellow human being.

When one has to deal with a complex situation concerning patient and relatives, I feel the best thing is simply to muster your courage and not to plan beforehand what to say or how to act. Such forethought is in itself a kind of defense that prevents one from being open to the situation. It would be more helpful to say to yourself: Whatever happens will happen, and I will just be there and listen.

We have discussed how extremely demanding relatives often have their own deep-seated fears, or they may be transferring their sense of guilt in relation to the patient onto the medical personnel. In this case, try to get a more detailed picture of the family situation as it was prior to the patient falling ill.

Forgiveness

If there is some degree of trust, one can tactfully broach the subject of guilt and mutual forgiveness. About the essence of forgiving, Vladika Anthony says that to forgive does not mean to forget. To forget is not forgiving. Forgiveness will begin at the moment when, while still feeling one's wound, one nevertheless is able to say: "Yes, I will take the person as he is, whatever pain he has caused me. I will accept him as Christ accepts me. If need be, I will carry him either as the lost sheep or as a cross on which I have to die in order for him to live. It is only at the cross that the words: 'Forgive him, Lord, he did not know what he was doing,' can be said, since the victim always receives the godly power to forgive sins."[23]

When a person cannot forgive the offender, he will become a prisoner of his own resentment. One can even say that the person who is "to blame" continues to have power over his victim, as long as his victim has not forgiven him. They are still deeply "knotted" together.

Alienation

It can happen that our behavior unintentionally conveys to the patient a feeling of being a mere object who does not matter to us as a person. As an example, here is a patient whose breathing is labored; he is gasping for breath. His doctor assesses his condition and goes away after prescribing a drug. The nurse enters with her injection, and cheerfully announces "a little prick," although for

---

23 Antonij mitr. *Surozhskij, Chelovek pered Bogom: O molitve Gospodnej*, iz gl. 3 "Put' podviga." Moskva: Fond Duhovnoe nasledie mitropolita Antoniya Surozhskogo, 2010 (Russian). [Metropolitan Anthony of Sourozh, *Man Before God: The Way of Discipline*, Ch.3 "The Lord's Prayer". (Moscow: Metropolitan Anthony of Sourozh Spiritual Foundation, 2010).]

the patient this does not mean a "little prick" at all but rather a procedure that he may particularly fear or dislike.

"This will make you feel better," says the efficient nurse before leaving him. In reality, neither the doctor nor the nurse will be coming back soon to check whether he actually is feeling better. Unconsciously, the patient will interpret this behavior gloomily and conclude: "This is all there is. They have done their duty and I can expect nothing more."

We have already discussed how important it is to remain with a person who feels agitated or fearful. This applies even more to a patient who has difficulty breathing or who is in physical pain. In my opinion, it is not enough just to administer the treatment and then to leave the patient. The patient needs someone to stay with him until he feels better and is able to cope. Someone needs to be with him to allay his fears for medical reasons as well as out of plain humanity. This is because fear and pain constrict the vessels in the body, which exacerbates breathing problems and causes further discomfort.

The concern of relatives, by contrast, can improve the physical condition of the loved one. Simply by being quietly present, their tender care conveys to the patient a sense of being loved, of not being a burden to them. This, more than anything else, will help the patient to relax. Relaxing, the patient literally becomes less "uptight," and there will be an easing of physical symptoms, especially breathing problems.

On the contrary, if a patient does not feel loved and has a sense of being a burden, he can conclude that there is nothing left to do but die. All hope has vanished.

For a short period, our hospice hosted Thomas, a young, twelve-year-old boy who had lost his mother. His father did visit him, but there seemed to be a lack of love and tenderness towards his son and Thomas deeply resented this. It was his grandfather who loved the boy deeply and, although ill himself, used to sit silently at his bedside for long hours. But Thomas, hoping against hope, also longed for his father's love. Suddenly, at the very point when he seemed to despair of this ever happening, he had a severe hemorrhage and died.

Medical Staff and Clergy

A feeling of alienation can also be caused by the "specialists" themselves: doctors, nurses, psychotherapists, priests. Sometimes their formal behavior, implied by their status and affirmed by their uniform, creates an excessive distance between themselves on one hand and the patient and relatives on the other. This kind of barrier makes it impossible for any real meeting to happen.

As I see it, such an identification with one's professional role is a form of defense and, often unconsciously, an attempt to avoid becoming closely involved in the patient's pain and fear. It can be seen as a refusal by the professional to interact with the patient on the same level, a rejection of openness and vulnerability.

The image of the all-knowing important doctor or the super-efficient nurse will do nothing to facilitate an open encounter. It is important to remember that there are things which the sick person knows and the professionals do not. Only the patient knows what it means to stand in front of death; we, the so-called "specialists," lack that knowledge. We do not as yet have this experience and therefore it is the patient who will, in a sense, be the "professor," not us.

If the professional understands this and tries to relate with reverence and tact to the mystery of death and dying, even without anything being put into words, the patient will feel respected. The patient's real position is acknowledged and, at a certain level, there is no difference between the patient and the medical professional or clergyman. However, in my experience, achieving this state of affairs is rare and difficult since it means a meeting of person to person.

I have met psychotherapists, even students, who are sure they know how to help severely ill patients and those who are dying. In fact, as we have already stated, one can never prepare a patient for death. We ourselves have not lived through this experience. Even so-called near-death experiences are related by people who have returned to the world of the living. This is different from death itself. According to Vladika Anthony, the one thing that can be done is to prepare a person for Life, and, if possible, long before he is actually standing in front of death.

The best way to help a patient face his present reality is by being next to him in deep silence and compassion. Words of advice are often hollow and inappropriate, although, if it seems right, one can share a personal experience of loss and grief with the patient and his relatives that may serve as a mirror for them to see themselves.

If the caregiver is a believer, he can silently pray for the patient and ask our Lord to be present. According to Vladika Anthony, Christ is always there but to invite Him is another matter. He was also convinced that Christ is present in each of us, thanks to the sacrament of Holy Communion. Therefore, one can simply rest in Him without saying anything while attending to a patient.

Inexperienced priests facing a dying patient for the first time may be at a loss about what to say or how to act other than reciting the required prayers, which entails the risk of hiding behind the rites and prayers of the Church. I have seen priests standing at the foot of the hospital bed, towering over a patient who was lying flat. The priest then hastily read the prayers to the patient who seemed unable to follow the words. As a result, there was no real contact between them.

I feel that this often deepens the patient's fear, rather than comforting him and bringing him closer to God. Moreover, at least in Russia, the sudden appearance of a priest will often mistakenly be seen as a sign of approaching death.

Vladika Anthony's experience was that a priest should, first of all, get to know the patient and his family. It is better if this can happen earlier than at the moment of death. He should inquire about the dying person's life and what concerns and fears may still be present. At the same time, Vladika advised his priests not to start with "shop talk" but rather begin by listening seriously to the patient's questions and doubts. Only after a relationship of trust has been formed should priest and patient start praying together.

It also happens that doctors or nurses can develop an antipathy towards certain patients and even pass judgement on them. A sudden and inexplicable dislike for a patient they may hardly know often signals the transference of unresolved problems in the caregivers themselves.

Consider, for example, a nurse who is admitting a patient for the first time. Immediately, in a disproportionate way, she dislikes his voice. If the nurse is honest, she will pause and ask herself what is going on: "Stop, where is this coming from? I hardly know this patient: what is making me react this way?" She may then realize, for example, that the voice sounds exactly like that of an uncle whom she could not bear to be around.

One must, first of all, be honest enough to acknowledge one's inappropriate reaction to a patient. Then to look at oneself to try to find the reason for this and stop the transference. In working through this the caregiver resolves a conflict hidden in his or her own past, which will benefit future patients as well.

The opposite can also happen: a patient or relative may immediately have something against a particular doctor or nurse. This also may point to a transference of a conflict in themselves, and has nothing to do with this particular doctor or nurse.

Other reasons for dislike may have to do with the patient's bad previous experiences or negative expectations and defenses. For young doctors and nurses, it is especially important to relate to much older patients with tact and respect. They are not "sweeties," or "cute old men." These are people in their own right who have a wealth of a life experience and are often highly educated.

To jolly them along, calling them immediately by their first name, trying to artificially cheer them up, is not what is needed. Not seeing who they are will leave them with a sense of depersonalization. In speaking with them, it is better to defer to their superior knowledge of life. One should say things like: "About that question of yours, I really do not know, I haven't yet come across this. Can you possibly share your experience?"

Communicating Through Silence

More than once, Vladika Anthony spoke on the topic of communication. For him, the culmination of any type of communication had to be silence. He said that as long as we need words to keep the relationship going, we have not yet reached the highest level of mutual understanding.

There are different kinds of wordless communication. It can happen that a restless patient finds peace through deep eye contact with another person. Such contact will give the patient a feeling of having been seen and understood in the midst of suffering and will ease the feeling of loneliness.

But communication is not always with a visible person. It has happened more than once that a patient who has been in a coma suddenly opens his eyes and begins staring at the ceiling in wonder, without a word. The patient has seen someone and they are communicating.

A few years ago, I was asked to go and see a woman whose mother was in a coma and near death. I found the daughter sitting in a chair, far removed from her mother. She was obviously apprehensive about what was going to happen. We talked a little, and then, together we sat next to her mother.

The daughter asked me to pray the prayers for the release of the soul with her and, halfway through, the mother suddenly opened her eyes, looked up, and smiled at someone she was evidently seeing above her. This lasted about five minutes; then she looked straight at her daughter with extremely clear eyes, sank back onto her pillows, and died peacefully.

As we have mentioned, a patient in a coma will hear everything that is being said. People have come out of their coma, and could repeat word for word what was said at their bedside. It is extremely important to warn the relatives not to talk over the head of an unconscious patient. Sometimes relatives will tactlessly ask: "How long will this go on?" or "What about the funeral arrangements?"

Learning to Acquire Silence

When a patient is dying and we want to be with him in silence, this means something more than maintaining a quiet physical presence. It means being with the dying patient in a state of such openness that the person will not be alone. On the contrary, the dying person will have the feeling that here is someone who wants to enter his loneliness as death approaches. We need to enter into the patient's situation from the depth of our being. In my own experience, nurses who are asked to sit with a dying patient can be found physically present, but they may be engrossed in a magazine, telephone, or an iPad. This is not what is meant by being *with* a dying patient, and it will have the opposite effect: the patient will feel even more alone.

It should be remembered that a seriously ill patient becomes very receptive to what is going on in the immediate environment. There was an American psychologist who described such incidents while working with the terminally ill and their nurses.

A dying patient was surrounded by his family. A nurse sitting in the corner of the room was thinking about the patient and said to herself: "What a pity, he is dying and he never wanted to face his diagnosis; what a fool!" At once the patient opened his eyes and asked the nurse to leave, saying: "She is bothering me." A little later, another nurse sitting with him thought how sad it was that she could not do anything for him, that she would like to help in some way. This time the patient immediately said to his relatives, "Let her stay, she does me good." This so clearly shows how not only our moods but our thoughts become a reality and have a direct effect on our surroundings.

This is what Vladika Anthony says about silence:

> Silence is not only a situation when we do not use words or are not uttering phrases. In essence, it is a condition of our inner state when thoughts have become still, the heart is at peace, the will is pointed in one direction only without any wavering: this we can learn under any circumstances. Silence of the emotions and of the body will take place when we cut off all unruly desires, such as curiosity.
>
> Curiosity will simply pull us away from ourselves, [so that] we are living outside ourselves. "Outside ourselves" because we will not settle down until we have found out about yet another thing.

From this follows anxiety of the mind and anxiety of the heart. One of the basic exercises we have to learn is to let go of everything in which our soul is entangled, of objects of curiosity, greed, fear, etc. The aim of this is to enter into oneself and, from within, to look at the world; not to be like an octopus that stretches his tentacles out in all directions and holds them there. We have to learn to become masters of ourselves: to remain within oneself and to act freely.

Vladika goes on to advise:

Come back under your skin, live under your skin; nothing else will be asked of you. Then it will be possible to act from within, and you will acquire silence.[24]

The key to real communication with the seriously ill patient lies in our ability to be silent without any defenses of our own, simply to be present at the patient's side without wanting anything to happen. Just be silent and perfectly at ease; wait quietly for what may occur.

When a new patient is admitted it is important to find out about negative experiences that the patient and his relatives may have had in the past in regard to medical treatment, illnesses, and dying. The memories of these events may be the reason for anxiety, lack of trust, or refusal to face the present situation.

In one of his lectures, Vladika Anthony talked about a nine-year-old boy who suffered a great deal. When asked how he had learned to take his suffering so calmly, he said: "I do not dwell on what I have already suffered, and I do not think about what might happen next. I simply live in the present moment."

This little boy showed so clearly what it means to live in the "here and now." How often we make our situation unbearable by multiplying our present trial with negative memories and pain of

24 Antonij mitr. Surozhskij, *Chelovek pered Bogom: Sozercanie i deyatel'nost'*. Moskva: Fond Duhovnoe nasledie mitropolita Antoniya Surozhskogo, 2010 (Russian). [Metropolitan Anthony of Sourozh, *Man Before God*, Ch..1: "Search, Contemplation, and Activity." (Moscow: Metropolitan Anthony of Sourozh Spiritual Foundation 2010.)]

the past. No one is asking us to carry all that has been and will be as one big cluster at this particular moment.

The only burden we have to endure is the one that is afflicting us at this moment. Vladika Anthony also speaks about this. He says that we would be able to endure our trials with greater ease if we did not make them so much heavier by multiplying them with our memories of pain from the past and our imagination of what might happen in the future. It will take a fair amount of discipline to learn to cut off such irrelevant emotions from the past and imaginations of the future in order to remain in the "here and now." However, this is exactly what is conducive to inner silence, and so needed when one wants to communicate with a person who is suffering and dying.

The Role of Prayer in Communicating with Seriously Ill Patients

From my experience, I would say that no one should be made to feel that he ought to listen to prayers or to be prayed for out loud if he has not asked for it. It can be frightening if the prayers are not understood or if the person praying is not in tune with the patient. It is my view that one can always pray silently, inwardly holding the person up to Christ and asking Him to be present and to heal His child who is so ill.

Vladika Anthony talks about the meaning of the word "intercession." It has to be taken literally, as the roots of the word imply: to step into the middle; to step into a crisis; to be in the eye of the storm. In prayer one does not only use words; certain actions have to follow, not only on the Lord's part but our own. We must be ready to step into the situation in a concrete way.

When everything possible has been done to lighten the condition of a suffering or dying patient but he is still not at peace, the need for prayer becomes even more acute.

In some cases, prayer will be accepted by the patient as a means to bring meaning to suffering, as I show here:

In a four-bed ward in the hospice, Nicholas, a simple man whom I had not met before, unexpectedly turned to me and asked, "Can you not give me an injection?" "In order to kill you?" I replied. He nodded. I told him that we did not work like that here. I looked at him and, why, I do not know, asked him: "Nicholas Sergeivich, do you know your patron saint, St. Nicholas?" He replied with a firm "Yes." "Then," I continued, "if you are really ready to go, not only in your body, but also in your soul, then ask St. Nicholas to be your advocate before God, for he knows you best." Nicholas smiled and enthusiastically put his thumb up. "I will ask St. Nicholas as well," I added and I left him. Within two days he died. He had been heard.

I think that when he made this appeal to St. Nicholas, it signaled that he did not have to wait passively for death. Rather, he was given a task that gave some meaning to his suffering and also meant that he himself had some control. This helped him to cope in a new way, with the assistance of the saint, of course!

Prayer is especially needed after a patient has died. It will be the only way of communicating and giving support to his soul. In the Eastern Orthodox Church, we pray for the soul of the departed in a special service called a *pannikhida*. We stand with lit candles as a sign of the light the person has been during his life. We ask God to give peace to him or her. These are words from the prayer at the end of the service:

> With the spirits of the righteous give rest, O Savior, to the souls of Thy departed servants and keep them in the blessed life with Thee, O Lover of man. In the place of Thy rest, O Lord, where all Thy saints repose, give rest also to the souls of Thy servants, for Thou alone art the Lover of mankind.
>
> With the saints give rest, O Christ, to the souls of Thy servants, where there is no pain, no sorrow, no sighing, but life everlasting.

Vladika Anthony advised people who were bereft by the death of a loved one to become still, to enter into themselves and to stand before the presence of God, then deep within the soul's meeting with God to find, in a new way, the departed who now is alive in God.

Obstacles to Communicating with Patients

It is not always easy to see and hear what a patient is actually saying. Often, we ourselves prevent a person from opening up to us by the way we behave. For example, Claire, who was seventeen years old and from an Orthodox family, was continuously praised for her courage during her illness. Her relatives praised her for her deep trust and faith in God and for the fact that she was never anxious or fearful. This attitude, I felt, was preventing Claire from talking about how she really felt. It made it almost impossible for her to say openly that she was frightened, that she felt so small, like a little girl who was in real need of support. When she lay dying, I glimpsed her eyes full of fear. Yet her relatives did not notice this, and they were still saying how brave she was. As a result, in spite of the many relatives who were constantly with her, she had to face everything alone.

Her relatives failed to see that they acted as a screen between Claire and themselves, and were not giving her room to become her real self. I think that unconsciously they felt unable to face reality themselves, or to enter fully into the pain and fear they were all experiencing.

Vladika Anthony mentions several reasons why we are often so reluctant to embrace suffering:

Fear

When faced with suffering, we all have to face the question of fear – our own fear, not anyone else's. It seems as though I will go to pieces as soon as I open up to the pain, as soon as I see and become aware of the suffering before me.

...Our participation in the life of the world, in the life of a person, in the life of Christ, will only begin when we can say: "Yes! Let it be like this!" To carry others, be it the whole world, be it a particular person, be it a group of exhausted people – to accept them means using an image of Christ: taking another person, someone else's suffering, upon one's shoulders.[25]

Anger

We often resort to anger so that the suffering will be less acute, less heart-rending. It is much easier to get angry about injustice in the world; it is much easier to be angry about the ones who have caused the suffering, and later about the person who suffers and wants our compassion, which we do not want to give.

... To suffer seems a passive state, to suffer means to surrender oneself, and as the Gospel says, to let people do as they want.... To get angry is easy; in anger there is some activity, there is a kind of truth (albeit an imaginary one) but still a strength. We feel that to suffer means being powerless, defenseless, and vulnerable. We feel that anger is generally a courageous reaction to evil in the world. However, by adopting this position we are depriving ourselves of participation in a stance towards the world and its suffering, that unavoidable pain that we find in Christ and in God.[26]

Shifting Responsibility onto Others

Often, we react to pain and suffering in two ways. Either we close down, we shut our eyes, we close our ears, we do not want to see... or we interpret it in our [own] way: "He suffers, yes! But who is to blame? He suffers, yes, but why should I respond? Is there really no one else? Is he really such a close friend to me

---

25 Antonij mitr. Surozhskij, "Chelovek pered Bogom: Vospitanie serdca, a ne trenirovka voli" [Metropolitan Anthony of Sourozh, *Man Before God: The Way of Discipline,* Ch. 3 "The Education of the Heart, Not the Training of the Will,"] ibid.

26 ibid

and I to him? Is there really nobody else who would be close to him in a more natural way?"[27]

When a person chooses to remain angry, he shifts his responsibility onto someone or something else: his destiny, his circumstances, or even onto God, instead of taking life into his own hands and working out his attitude towards this situation. This, again, is the position of being merely a victim, which has already been discussed.

The Oneness of Body and Soul

Our body and soul are closely related: what happens to our soul will affect our body and what happens to the body will have an impact on the soul. Vladika Anthony says, "If you study psychology and physiology you discover... on the level of simple and rather elementary physiology, that every psychological event, every emotional event, every intellectual activity, results in glandular changes, muscular changes, and so on."[28] This is another reason why it is so important to face one's pain and grief, to live through it and not to suppress it. When this has not happened, there will inevitably be repercussions at a later stage on a physical level caused by the unresolved grief.

It is also necessary to realize what impact our own energies (positive or negative) have on each person we meet. It sometimes happens that a nurse enters a room at a time when the patient has just fallen asleep and there is a deep stillness in the air. But too often, it is as if a whirlwind has blown in: the silence is broken and the patient is woken up by the breeziness and efficiency of the nurse. More often than not, she is not aware of this, although the patient is.

---

27 ibid

28 Metropolitan Anthony of Sourozh, "Body and Matter in Spiritual Life" in *Sacrament and Image: Essays in the Christian Understanding of Man.* Ed. A.M. Allchin, (London: Fellowship of S. Alban and S. Sergius, 1967) p 33-41. http://masarchive.org/Sites/texts/1967-00-00-1-E-E-T-EW00-008Body&MatterInSpiritualLife.html

As I said previously, being able to read the sick person's body language is important for us when dealing with patients, but the reverse is also true: patients will be reading our body language. The patient will intuitively note and understand the body language of his doctors, nurses, and the relatives who have gathered around. After all, the patient has plenty of time to observe and assess them.

I remember one young woman in the hospice who, after she had been there for a while, said to me: "You know, at first it seemed to me that this place was like heaven, but now I see that it is all done mechanically. The nurses are smiling, even kind perhaps, but everything is done out of sheer habit."

She felt that she had not been seen as a unique person, but as "one more patient," on whom the staff had to perform certain procedures. Our bodies, unbeknownst to us, will express very accurately how we feel and relate to others. A patient will know, for example, by looking into our eyes that we are fearful or that we are casting judgement. One should make the relatives aware of this as well, because if there is a wall of secrecy, falsehood, or simply holding back between them, the sick person will certainly read this in their body language, which will increase the patient's own fear and loneliness.

Another important aspect of communication is touching. Our innermost feelings about a patient will be expressed very accurately by the way we touch that person's body: how we put a hand on the shoulder or try to find him a more comfortable position or turn him on the other side to prevent bedsores. Touch can be the first step to building a relationship of trust and real communication.

Here is such an example:

At forty-five years old, Viktor had a tumor of the spine that had left him paralyzed. He stayed in the hospice for a long period of time and this made it possible to develop a good relationship with him and his wife Nina. One day, I asked, as if I had forgotten, "Tell me, Viktor, I do not quite remember, what again is your diagnosis?" He looked straight at me and said it was osteoporosis. "Osteoporosis?" I repeated. "Yes, osteoporosis," he answered. His wife, however, knew that he had cancer and would die. Before coming in every day, she would wipe away her tears, and with a false smile and sad, red eyes she would greet her husband cheerfully.

One day I happened to catch Viktor's eye as he watched her come into the ward, her expression full of anxiety. It was then that I decided to talk to Nina and ask her whether it would perhaps be better to discuss openly with her husband about what was going on. She agreed and asked me to come with her, as she felt a little afraid. We went in together. I do not remember how we started, only that Viktor said: "But I knew from the very beginning that it was not osteoporosis, but cancer." They began crying and hugging each other so I left. The wall of pretense between them had fallen down.

The body language of a sick person has to be observed carefully. In the course of a conversation, the patient may suddenly shift his position in bed by turning away or coming closer. There may be a sudden clenching of fists when the medical situation is being discussed. From a relaxed position, the patient may start to cross his arms, as if to say, "Do not come too close to me." Or his tone of voice may deepen, when he begins to talk about something that is difficult to express or very close to the heart.

The patient may say that all is fine, although you observe a tightening of the lips; or he may be smiling but with sad or tense eyes. It can also be illuminating to note the subjects the patient does not mention.

However, the patient should always be in charge, that is, in the role of "host," while we as caregivers are mere "guests". If a patient is obviously in distress but does not want to talk about the reason, one can, without words and through eye contact, send the signal that this distress has been seen and accepted. This might make it easier for the patient to speak later.

Assessment through Body Language

When a patient is in a coma or otherwise unable to describe any complaints, it is only through body language that we will know how to offer support. When a comatose patient is restless, we have to find out the reason. For example, if there is a brain tumor, the restlessness may indicate a severe headache due to raised blood pressure. When the patient is very weak or taking certain drugs, restlessness may result from being constipated or having a full bladder with retention of urine. Also, a patient in a coma needs the same pain control as a conscious one. A woman told me recently that a friend of hers had come out of a coma after a year. The recovering patient said she had heard literally everything said around her, and that her head had felt on fire with pain all that time.

There can also be emotional or spiritual reasons for an unconscious person's restlessness, such as fear, anger, or a feeling of loneliness. There can be feelings of guilt or repentance, which may come when the person has a clear vision of everything that has happened in life up until now.

Through close observation of body language, one can more or less predict whether a patient is close to death or not. This is of importance in order to warn the relatives and see whether they want to stay close until the end.

There are certain definite signs which indicate that death is very close. There can be a sudden sharpening of the nose or a certain pale greenish-white color around the mouth; also, cyanosis (bluing) of the fingernails and toenails and also of the fingers and toes themselves. Another sign of impending death can be observed on the knees, which take on a mottled blueish-red color and feel cold to the touch. The breathing often changes, and there may be a rattling sound or apnea (suspension of breathing) when the patient takes long pauses between each breath. The heart rate will be irregular or very faint and, naturally, the blood pressure will continue to fall.

Nonphysical signs can include a very definite and almost tangible stillness which "hovers," as it were, around the patient. With very young children, I have more than once noticed the special sweet aroma that one sometimes smells from newly born babies.

As we have already discussed, there are a few patients who after being comatose for some time, will suddenly, when the end is near, open their eyes. With a clear and definite look (often of amazement and never of fear), they can be seen gazing upwards at something or someone present above them. This is something they see with calm and clear eyes – and therefore, to my mind, it cannot simply be ascribed to a hallucination caused by drugs.

It needs to be repeated that a dying patient, whether in a coma or not, will be able to hear to the very last moment, despite being unable to talk. Communication can certainly continue to the end, and those around can both talk and pray silently or out loud. Through touch or hand-holding, the dying person can be reassured that there is no risk of being left alone. Touch will be felt to the very last moment.

After a person has died, something beautiful can occur. Sometimes all of the suffering and pain which had marked the patient's face gradually fades away, replaced by a deep sense of stillness and peace.

Building Trust Through Touch

From the way we touch his or her body, a patient will gain a sense of our real attitude, a direct and true insight into who we caregivers really are, as opposed to how we present ourselves. Our touch can be rough, brusque, mechanical or it can be tender, caring, and respectful. It depends very much on ourselves whether a relationship of trust with the sick person can be built.

It is also worthwhile to try to put ourselves in the place of the patient who is lying flat, looking up at us from below. If we can do this, we may get an inkling of what the bedbound person is facing. Often, especially during the doctor's round, the medical staff all tower over the patient in a rather intimidating way. We are looking at the body rather than the person, and making a public clinical assessment of the pathologies and wounds. The way we sit or stand, close to or far from the patient, will say a lot about how we feel about that person.

I feel that it is much better for the caregiver or relative to sit down right next to the patient, as opposed to trying to communicate while standing at the foot of the bed. When we sit slightly lower than the patient, this sends an unconscious signal of respect and gives the patient the feeling of being, literally and metaphorically, on top.

I have often met relatives who feel that they have failed their loved ones by letting them go into a hospice. Perhaps this reflects a characteristic of Russian society, a feeling that a hospice must be an awful place whose only purpose is to provide a space to die.

Nevertheless, these relatives may feel guilty of betrayal and it is important to bring these feelings into the open. At times it may be appropriate to praise the relatives for having coped on their own for so long with the burden of care. One can make the point that a hospice has the capacity to monitor a patient continuously and respond to every new symptom. This means that either for a shorter or longer period this may be a better solution than family care, even when a good team is available at home. It also can be seen as respite care to give the relatives time to regain their own strength.

One can also talk to relatives about the fears they experienced, especially at night, when they were on their own with the patient: the sense of not knowing what to expect next and feeling helpless and anxious. One particular challenge when looking after a very sick person at home, especially if the patient is large and heavy, is the need to prevent pressure sores by making frequent changes of position, day and night. One should not underestimate the fatigue that accumulates for someone who has been looking after a very sick person at home over a long period of time; both anxiety and exhaustion will be greatly relieved once the patient is in the hospice.

Several relatives working together as caretakers will be able to support one another by spending some quiet time together and getting some rest. Their nervousness will decrease and they will no longer be at risk of having a negative psychological or even physical influence on their sick loved one.

When relatives have a feeling of having failed their loved one, all of the advantages of turning to a hospice can be gently discussed. When a patient's death draws near, relatives can feel helpless and unsure of what to do. The truth is that simply their presence, rather than any particular gesture or action, will help the patient more than anything. The person will be reassured that there is no risk of dying alone. On the contrary, the people whom he or she has loved over an entire life will be present to the very end. This in itself will make the person more relaxed and less "uptight." As a result, the patient will suffer less, physically and emotionally.

More than once I have seen a patient, who was barely alive and already showed signs of cyanosis (turning blue) in the hands and feet, rally when a close relative or friend appeared. I observed how, as an immediate result of the visit, the cyanosis disappeared and breathing improved. At least for a time, the specter of immediate death was gone.

We have already discussed how important it is to master oneself so as to be able to sit quietly with a dying person without an anxious feeling of needing to do something active and useful the whole time. This need for quiet self-control applies especially to relatives.

In regard to this restlessness, I once said to a relative named Galina (we had come to know each other quite well), "You run around your husband just like a chicken." At first, she looked slightly offended, then it became a little joke between us. Anyway, my words had their effect and Galina calmed down.

With relatives it is not a question of entirely suppressing fear and anxiety, because that is impossible. The main thing is that they should try not to be overpowered by these feelings. If they surrender to these feelings it will make their loved one worse, given the close bonds between them.

The Body is More than a Shell

When talking to relatives, one should stress that our body is not a mere outer shell, although very often one hears people saying exactly that. When someone has died, we do not simply throw the body away, as though it had not been a real part of that person. On the contrary, the body of a person whom we have loved during life should be regarded and treated with respect. This attitude of reverence for the body can be sensed in the "Service for the Departed" in the Orthodox Church, where the body is considered as important as the soul and the spirit.

Vladika Anthony was fully aware of the importance and role of the body:

> The body is not a piece of cloth which we simply throw off. The body is real in the same way as the whole of a person is real, as real as the soul. Only in the oneness of the body and the soul do we become a full person.
>
> Saint Isaac the Syrian expresses this thought in an unexpected and perhaps astonishing way. He says that the eternal destiny of man will not be decided before the resurrection of the body, since the body is on an equal level with the soul and the spirit and will play a part in determining this person's eternal destiny. The meaning of this saying has not been revealed to us, and we cannot imagine how this will be possible. And yet – yes: "me" is my body, on the same level as my soul, and we can only look at a person in his wholeness.[29]

It is through our body that we express our tenderness, our love, and all of our emotions. I can illustrate this with an unforgettable event that took place in a large English hospital with a little girl of five, whose mother I helped as an interpreter:

> The girl was being operated on for a severe heart problem, while her mother Niki and I waited in the corridor next to the doors of the operating theatre. After a long while the surgeon came out and said to the mother: "I am so sorry, your daughter has

29 Antonij mitr. Surozhskij "Zhizn'. Bolezn'. Smert': Celostnyj chelovek." (Moskva: Fond Duhovnoe nasledie Mitropolita Antoniya Surozhskogo, 2010) (Russian). [*Metropolitan Anthony of Sourozh*, "Life. Illness. Death: The Whole Human Person." (Moscow: Metropolitan Anthony of Sourozh Spiritual Foundation, 2010).]

just died." Niki immediately started screaming. She fell to the ground and began rolling about, expressing her unbearable grief in a very physical way. This was a despair and sorrow so deep that it could not be expressed in words, only through her body.

To this day, I am grateful to the surgeon, who was from Egypt and who simply stood there silently. He also understood that this was the only way to let the mother start living her grief. He did not offer her any comfort through hollow words; he did not go and fetch tranquilizers to suppress her emotions. He let her be, without a word, and we simply stayed with her.

Let me give another example from our hospice in Moscow:

A six-year-old boy called Kirill was dying of a brain tumor, and his mother Catherine spent the whole time with him in a single-bed room. When Kirill eventually died, she began screaming at the top of her voice. She refused tranquilizers and turned away any attempts by the nurses to show compassion. On the contrary, she gave us to understand: "Leave me alone, do not come near me, do not touch me, I want to be alone in my grief."

Sitting on the floor, she began to sway backwards and forwards, and cried and cried.

This went on for a long time, until suddenly she stood up, looked around, and began speaking as she held and caressed her little son on her lap. "How strange, I have no tears left and I feel so calm."

The only immediate way for Catherine to express her pain was through her body. Bodily actions helped her to face the reality of her loss in an immediate and concrete way.

CHAPTER FIVE

Fears That Can Trouble a Seriously Ill Patient

When a patient feels unable to express certain feelings, fear in particular, this frustration can itself lead to a worsening of physical symptoms. Such symptoms can include a change in blood pressure, constipation, nausea, severe headaches, and insomnia. These symptoms may get steadily worse unless there is sensitive support from relatives and medical staff.

In order to provide this kind of support, it helps to itemize the various kinds of fear that a dying person can experience. They include:

1. The fear of pain and of losing control as a result.
2. The fear of separation.
3. The fear of losing one's identity.
4. The fear of having no existence after death.
5. The fear of becoming a burden.
6. The fear of meeting God, our Creator.
7. The fear of endless suffering, the uncertainty of its duration.
8. The fear of losing one's outer appearance.
9. The fear of having to die without having lived to the full.
10. The fear of losing one's financial position.
11. The fear of losing one's social setting.

Some of these fears have already been discussed, so I will not repeat them but I would like to discuss some of the fears that I have observed and talked over with gravely ill patients in both Russia and England.

It is worth mentioning that questions of life and death in Russia are still affected by the country's tragic history. Throughout the seven decades of communism, materialist views prevailed and discussion of death was taboo. It was as though the existence of death was denied. That may mean that the fear of death and of facing up to the reality that death is a part of life is more acute in Russia than in the West.

Then there is the question of euthanasia, to which different cultures bring different perspectives. The rising popularity of euthanasia in many countries seems to me a symptom of a problem which is more common in the West: a refusal to find meaning in suffering. In other words, this phenomenon reflects a fear of the process of suffering and dying, as opposed to an acceptance of that process.

It seems that when people speak about euthanasia, they usually have in mind the body which is supposedly "ready" to expire. But this concerns only the physical side of illness.

Other questions also need to be asked. The body may supposedly be ready, but what about the soul? What is the state of the soul, not only emotionally but spiritually? Is the soul ready as well? Has it been cleansed of all of the negative emotions, thoughts and deeds which have been accumulated in the course of a life? In my experience, when a person is ready both in body and soul, he will be able to let go and die.

For the believer, the decision to end it all is clearly saying: "God, I do not trust You, nor do I have any hope that You will ever change my situation. I know better than You." However, the question of euthanasia is a desperate cry for help.

Faced with extreme suffering, it is the responsibility of the people around, be they doctors, psychotherapists or clergy, to care for and love these patients so deeply that their pain can be alleviated, to show such concern and tenderness that they can find meaning even in their seemingly hopeless situation.

A patient who has been diagnosed with a serious illness such as cancer often ponders the question: "What if the pain becomes so severe that nothing will be able to take it away?"

To answer this, one can make the point that nowadays, at least in the hospice setting, pain control is so advanced that in nearly all cases (more than 80%) the symptoms can be dealt with.

However, if it is a question of relieving the breathlessness which may arise in lung cancer or with cancer that has spread from elsewhere to the lung, then I feel that one has to be truthful. It may not be possible to relieve the breathlessness entirely, but everything will be done to make things easier, and the patient will not be left alone. That is a promise, of course, that has to be kept.

Many patients and relatives fear or oppose the idea of using morphine to alleviate severe pain or breathlessness. There is a common worry that it will turn into an addiction. One should explain that in situations that require pain relief, the amount of morphine given will correspond to the intensity of the pain. The two things will level each other out and there will be no risk of addiction.

The fear of pain is closely connected to the fear of losing control; the patient may worry that by losing control, he will forfeit his dignity as a person. It is often difficult and shameful for a patient to have lost control over his reactions and emotions, and there may be a sense of losing one's personality. I think we then have to convey to the patient that he or she is not simply reducible to an illness. The patient must be encouraged to hold onto the sense of being a unique person, created in the image of God. It can be pointed out that deep within the soul there is a precious treasure, the core of our true identity, which *cannot* be reduced to nothingness by illness or even by death itself. This may emerge in the course of discussions with the patient, but there are also other ways of conveying this truth: in the way we care for the patient and show our respect, and in the way we use touch and eye contact to deliver nonverbal messages.

In our hospice, a patient called John wrote me the following note: "I am now good for nothing, I am of no use to anyone anymore." He could hardly speak, because of the tracheostomy tube that had been inserted into his throat. It was clear that he had lost all self-respect and hope.

It took a long time for him to accept that he had an inner worth that was independent of his outer circumstances. This had to be demonstrated to him, not so much through talking as by showing him continuous respect and care, by taking the time to communicate, even if this could only be done through writing.

As illness progresses, many patients feel helpless and vulnerable. Often, they experience their dependence on others as shameful, and themselves a burden to their relatives and friends. When this fear of being a burden arises, one has to address it openly to help the patient find meaning in suffering and in what is happening to everyone involved in his life.

I remember a story about a young nun who lived in France at the end of the nineteenth century. She suffered a great deal, very courageously. One day a bishop came to visit her and asked what her monastic job was. She gave him the following answer: "Being ill." By this she meant that sickness was her particular task, her responsibility.

To me, this is a beautiful illustration of how to look at one's illness and suffering not only on a physical level but also on an emotional and spiritual level, as a concrete "task." We can consciously take responsibility for the way we deal with and face up to our illnesses. This in turn may be an inspiration to others.

As was this instance:

Simon had been in our hospice for a good while. He was paralyzed from the waist down because of a spinal tumor, yet on a certain level all seemed to be going well with him and his wife Nadia. They were together in a single-bed room, and Nadia often asked the nurses to have a cup of tea with them after work. It all seemed so pleasant in spite of the illness. Then, one evening, Simon said to me out of the blue: "Frederica, I want to make an end of it all, I cannot go on like this." I did not say much in reply to this: only that it would not be an answer to his problem. I simply left it at that.

Then a few days later, he said to me: "Frederica, I do not want to kill myself any longer." I wondered what had happened and he explained: "God has shown me that I have a special task to fulfil." "What type of task?" I asked, with real curiosity. "He has shown me that I will be a guide for everyone, especially for Nadia, when they come to the next world after me."

It needs to be said that Simon was not a man of particularly deep faith, and yet this was enough to make him want to continue living. He had found a meaning in his suffering and impending death.

Drawing on his experience in the concentration camps, Viktor Frankl says, "If there is a meaning in life at all, then there must be a meaning in suffering. Suffering is an ineradicable part of life, as is fate and death. Without suffering and death, human life cannot be complete."[30]

Almost all patients find it difficult that, in their view, they have become a burden. Especially for men, this can be a serious problem. To learn to "be" but not to be active as they once were, to accept help from others, can seem a defeat, as if they have lost their personality and worth in life.

Vladika Anthony warns about this feeling of being a burden. He says it is a cry of despair that has to be fully addressed. In his view, instead of accepting this pessimistic idea, one should suggest that, on the contrary, the patient is giving relatives the opportunity to learn something great: the opportunity to learn to love in spite of tiredness and the feeling of having no strength left. These relatives are learning to forget about themselves and stick faithfully to the duty of care. In other words, the patient is giving them the great gift of acquiring sacrificial love, which is a quality of eternal life that is rare nowadays.

It is a good thing when people who are looking after their ill parents realize at a deep level that their roles in life have been reversed. They were brought up by their parents; now it is their turn to care for their parents, not out of a feeling of duty but out of love. As I see it, one has to speak about this openly.

30 Frankl, p 88.

A patient who is inactive and bedbound can be encouraged to find other tasks in life. Being busy is no longer possible, but now there is an opportunity to be a haven of stillness and quiet for others. If the patient is a believer, he can be of great help by offering prayers and intercession for friends and relatives. Even wordless prayer can be a way to send loved ones some warmth and tenderness. The patient can ask God to send His blessing on each person that he or she has ever known – not only the living but on the departed as well.

The patient can thank God for the saints who are so alive in God. Another "task" for the patient is simply to respond with dignity to one's highest calling as a human being: to be an example for others and to show how it is possible to suffer and prepare for one's death in a courageous way. It may be possible to convey the idea that in this way, the patient can offer their relatives something of lasting benefit – the ability, at some later time, to face their own suffering and death.

The Fear of Endless Suffering

A fear can also arise of having to suffer interminably, not knowing when it will end. This fear, combined with the deep tiredness that long illness can cause, leads some people to think about euthanasia. Frankl wrote that in the concentration camps, one of the most severe trials for the prisoners was not knowing when their time in the camp would end. This question, "When will it all be finished?" torments patients and relatives alike.

Unfortunately, this sort of question is often asked in the presence of the patient who may seem to be asleep or in a coma. One has to remind the relatives who are asking such questions that the patient will hear everything that is being said till the very end, so any discussions of this sort are best conducted somewhere else.

When questions about "how long this will last" come from a patient who is already exhausted by illness, and if it seems clear that the end is not too distant, I give a straight answer by saying something like: "It is not long now, try to have just a little more patience," and at the same time I assure them that they will not be left alone.

Sometimes communication with words is difficult or impossible, as in this case:

I remember a fifty-year-old patient called George. He himself was a psychologist and at the first meeting with the nurses, he said firmly: "Do not give me any advice, I know it all myself." It was a good thing that, as an acupuncturist, I had no need to talk when I treated him. In fact, body and pulse diagnosis is even better done in silence. Treating him meant sitting next to him in silence for half an hour.

Of course, he would study me as I worked on him but without speaking a word. One day while I was with him, my eye fell upon a very sharp knife lying on his night table. I knew that he did not eat any more, and certainly was not peeling fruit. It was obvious to me that he did not need this knife any longer and I wondered if he might be considering ending it all.

I discussed this with the doctor in charge and we decided to take the knife from him. I came back to George and told him that this knife was bothering me. He looked at me and said: "What nonsense!" I replied: "Well, if it's such nonsense, then I *will* take it away." Interestingly, he did not object to this at all.

A few days later, while treating him, I suddenly started telling him about an impressive dream that one of my friends had told me concerning her two brothers who were long dead. The younger one, John, had perished in World War II. When the older one, Peter, learned of John's death, he took his own life.

In the dream, which happened many years later, she saw them both. John was looking very peaceful, busy drawing something. She asked him how he was and he said: "Oh, I am so happy, it is so good to be here." Then she was shown her other brother, Peter, who was sitting somewhere in a corner, looking rather sad. She asked him: "Are you feeling poorly?

Do they not love you there?" He answered: "No, you do not understand: everyone who comes here has been called, invited to come, but I came of my own will."

After telling George this, I kept silent for a little while. Then, in spite of his rejection of advice, I simply said to him: "Stick it out for a little while, it will not be long." He did not reply to this, but as I left, George, for the first time, said "Thank you." To this day, I do not know whether he was referring to the treatment or to the story about the dream. Within a few days, he peacefully reposed.

Most people are afraid of the unknown. That is why dying patients are sometimes fearful and apprehensive about the moment of death and what comes next. When such feelings emerge, it is good to find out if the patient has previously experienced someone close dying and what images they have from that.

You can also ask gently about other related attitudes. Here, I vividly remember Sergei, a patient who was dying of metastasized throat cancer. He had adamantly refused any chemotherapy or radiation and, when I asked why, he told me that seven people in his family had died of cancer. All of them had undergone this kind of treatment and it had produced no positive result but only seemed to make them worse.

When a patient voices fear over what exactly will happen at death, it is important to sit down and have an honest discussion: to say that nobody knows exactly what will happen because no one living now has experienced death. One can even say that the patient has a more real and deeper experience of what this means than the caregivers.

I am convinced that it is necessary to help bring these questions and fears to the surface. Once they have been brought into the open, fear will almost certainly have less of a hold on the patient.

It sometimes happens, however, that a patient refuses to look honestly at their situation or to confront their fears.

Vladika Anthony spoke of such a patient:

I remember visiting a very frightened lady [with cancer] who resisted any attempt to establish simple, direct contact…. Then I said to her: "How great, that you have neither death nor serious illness hanging over you," and in the process of talking to one another, I began to share how my own mother who, having been diagnosed with cancer, had died.

We spoke for a long time about everything my mother and I had lived through, and in the end, this lady asked, "What do you think. Would I be able, like your mother, to face my death as she did?" Now we could begin to talk about herself, and not about my mother.[31]

More than once I have seen how it can help to tell a story in the third person about someone who has lived through an experience similar to the patient. This can help the patient to look at his or her own situation from another angle.

When a patient is a believer with a real conviction of the reality of God, there can be a fear of meeting Him after death. However, I have noticed that rarely will such fear be present if during one's lifetime there has been a personal experience of God's presence and His love. There may be a sense of awe and trepidation, but not of actual fear.

Vladika Anthony stressed many times that Christ is, in the first place, our Saviour and not only our Judge. Through His incarnation, He took upon Himself every aspect of our condition as human persons (while remaining without sin), and is in complete solidarity with us.

The fear of meeting one's Creator may be connected, I think, with unresolved conflicts or unconfessed sins. If the latter is the case, and the patient has expressed the wish to see a priest, one can provide support for this.

Some people are afraid of simply falling into nothingness after death. At first, that may seem strange, for if there were "nothing" on the horizon, then one should have nothing to fear, but in fact, this is linked to the fear of losing one's identity.

31 Antonij mitr. Surozhskij, "Pastyr' u posteli bol'nogo iz gl. Materiya i Duh" [Metropolitan Anthony of Sourozh, "Pastoral Care of the Sick and Dying."], ibid.

We have already discussed how a seriously ill patient loses his former ways of negotiating life: his social contacts, his ability to work and earn a living, his position in the family, and so on. This is especially difficult for those who have always identified their worth and significance in the world with their achievements. Instead of asking questions like "Am I successful?" or "Do I earn a lot of money?" the person now faces existence in a state of nakedness and vulnerability and must confront questions like, "What has been the meaning of my life?"

Previous strategies for life do not help any more. Ultimately, the only thing that now becomes important is love, the only thing that continues after death. This fear of losing control seems to me connected with a refusal to accept the reality of one's situation, which has changed completely. It may also be an expression of deep-seated fears that came into being earlier in the person's life. Fear and the desire to control are closely interwoven.

The fear of losing control may be allayed by fostering a capacity to live in the "here and now" and by developing the discipline of not allowing memories of the past or fears of the future to overpower the present situation. The opposite of control is an attitude of trust. "What will happen will be the best thing for me; it is up to me to accept it and bear it with dignity."

According to Vladika Anthony, the fear of separation will appear when the patient realizes that the illness is terminal. Most people have no real faith in life after death and no real sense that life will continue – differently, but it will continue. Often, when I enquire about a patient's beliefs in life after death, I get the answer, "There is probably something." Seldom is the answer, "There will be Someone." However, when I ask, for instance, an elderly patient who clearly stated that she did not believe that there was any life after death, whether she feels that her mother, who died long ago, is alive or not, she will often say, "Oh yes, I have seen her in a dream, she helps me all the time."

The same people may have similar feelings about the saints to whom they turn in daily life. So, are they dead? If the saints are alive, having been the same human beings as we are (the only difference being, that during their life, they loved God with real depth), doesn't that suggest that we too will continue to live after death?

I believe it is important to put this sort of question to patients and, if appropriate, to relatives. In this way, one can help them see that they already have an experience of eternity.

As we have noted from the words of Vladika Anthony, this will reduce the fear of death and somehow lessens the pain of separation. Not in the sense that there will not be a separation and that it will not be painful, but that it is only temporary, not forever, and that in the future there will be a joyful meeting with the beloved, who is truly alive. And even now, according to Vladika Anthony, to the extent in which we ourselves are deeply rooted in God in prayer and silence, we will be one with the departed already here on earth in a new and deeper way, since he is now alive in God.

Sometimes, I share with patients (and especially with distressed relatives) my own experiences of grief and separation. I tell them how all of the people I have lost are alive to me, and at times quite obviously supporting me.

Even if a patient is not a believer, I feel that if one simply talks about these things from one's own experience, this will resonate and give some hope.

Here is another story based on an incident described to me by a friend. Her mother had died many years before, but at a certain moment when my friend was in pain, she cried out impulsively, "Mama, where are you?? I do not see you!" Her mother then appeared to her in a dream with words of comfort, "My beloved little daughter, I hear and know everything."

The pain of separation is very noticeable among teenagers and young adults who are dying, but usually they are more concerned about their parents than about themselves. Frequently, they are only thinking, "How will my parents cope without me?" I have often felt deeply touched watching these dying youngsters gradually prepare their parents for their death and for the coming separation. More often than not, they are the ones giving comfort to their parents, rather than the other way around.

We can see this here:

Igor was nineteen years old and short of breath as a result of his lung cancer. He and his mother were close and had no secrets from each other; they discussed everything openly. Finally, his hemoglobin level dropped severely which made his breathlessness worse and he was transferred to another hospital for a blood transfusion. He was brought back to the hospice at the weekend, but died the following day.

When I met Igor's mother on the following Monday, she told me what had happened: "When Igor returned to the hospice yesterday, he felt very poorly, he was suffering a lot. I went out of the room and begged God to do whatever was best for Igor. I said that I was ready to let him go. When I came back and told Igor what I had said to God, his answer was: 'Mama, you finally understood!' A little later, I started to talk to him about what we would do the following Wednesday, but he looked at me intently and said: 'No, Mama, on Wednesday I will no longer be here.'"

Before he died, Igor gave instructions as to how he would like to be buried, and what to give to his friends. He also cared very much about his brother: he asked his mother to look after him well, and his brother to do the same for his mother. This is not a rare example of how young adults or teenagers who are terminally ill can accept their illness and prepare their parents for their coming death with great dignity.

Here is another example:

Tonia was sixteen years old. She played the violin and had already given many performances. When she gave me a compact disc of one of her concerts, I listened to it in amazement. This was not the performance of a sixteen-year-old girl, but of a mature woman who had insight into the depth and richness of life.

Tonia supported her mother and helped her to accept her coming death. Tonia was not afraid, and told her mother how her late grandmother had appeared to her in a dream and said that she was waiting for her. Her mother sometimes shared her bed in the hospice, and they often embraced each other in preparation for the coming separation. Like so many teenagers in this situation, Tonia was able to help her mother to accept her approaching death through her own courage and fearlessness.

When a married person is dying, the partner who is about to be left behind may have an acute fear of the coming loneliness. In addition, the soon-to-be bereaved person can be anxious about no longer being seen as a part of a couple, but as a single widowed person for whom all aspects of social life will change. Later in this book we will discuss the tasks and aims that the bereaved can set themselves. These aims can act as keys to mustering the courage to continue in spite of what feels, at times, like searing pain combined with utter loneliness.

When there is a sudden diagnosis of a serious illness, people can have a desperate feeling that they have not yet really begun to live a full life, and now it is too late.

Here again is Vladika Anthony:

> In one of his letters, the Apostle Paul says that we should value time because the days are deceptive. And indeed, does time not deceive us? Is it not true that we spend the days of our life as if, in a slapdash and careless manner, we are writing a rough copy of our life, which we will one day rewrite?.... We live in this way year in, year out, without fully, completely, and perfectly doing all that we could have done, because "there is still time." "This we can finish later, that we will do afterwards when we write the clean copy."[32]

---

32 *Antonij mitr. Surozhskij,* "Zhizn'. Bolezn'. Smert': Pamyat' smertnaya." [*Metropolitan Anthony of Sourozh,* Life. Illness. Death.: Remembrance of Death.] Ibid.

Often during my lectures (to doctors, nurses, psychology students, social workers and theological students), I have asked the following question:

"How would you feel if you were told today that you had only three months to live?" Almost all of my listeners acknowledge that they have not yet started to live fully, and imagine the horror they would feel at the fact there is now little time left. Secondly, there was the frequent reply: "How can I leave my loved ones behind?"

CHAPTER SIX

If a Patient Is Unable to Speak

When a dying patient is unable to speak, relatives often ask, "What do we do?" It would actually be better to ask this question the other way around: "What not to do when a patient is unable to speak?" As we have remarked, relatives will often ask, right in the presence of the patient, when it will all be over, if it will be much longer, or what to do next and how to prepare the funeral arrangements. The patient can interpret this as something like: "When will he finally die, when will it all be over?" I wonder how I would feel if I heard this, without being able to say a word because of cancer, a coma, or simply because of extreme weakness prior to death. Once again, one has to remember that a dying patient, in a coma or not, will hear everything until the last moment!

When relatives ask such questions, this indicates that they are not present in the moment, in the "here and now," but are already in the future, planning the next steps. This desire to plan is natural, but it is important not to miss the precious chance to be here in the "now" with this person in the last moments of his life.

As one realizes how the feelings and emotions of those around a patient affect that person's welfare, something important becomes clear. We have a huge responsibility to behave appropriately in the presence of every patient. When a patient is unable to talk, in a coma, or seemingly just in a continuous deep sleep, the relatives often think that because there is no response it is of no use to stay with their loved one. However, as we have already discussed, it is precisely the case that the mere presence of a relative will be a great support to the patient.

There are so many other ways of communicating one's love for someone who cannot respond physically. For example, through bodily contact: through our touch, through the caresses we offer, through our tone of voice. We can send a signal to our loved one through the care we take to arrange the pillows in a more comfortable position. If one is a believer, we can reach the depths of a loved one's soul through prayer, since in the silence of a prayerful encounter, words are not needed.

In my experience, almost all patients who are close to death would like to have someone present. To die alone, to be left to face death without any human warmth, is a hard ordeal. If relatives have enough love for the patient that they can stay until the end in spite of their physical and emotional exhaustion, or even fear, the patient will sense that he is not forgotten and will find it easier to obtain inner peace. If this has not been understood, we should speak about this with the relatives. When a relative finds it difficult to be near the patient, whether out of fear of death or of what to expect next, the best thing is for the doctor or nurse to sit down with this relative and offer some reassurance. We can make a point by holding the patient's hand or moistening his lips. When the relatives see this being done, their feeling of helplessness or fear of touching their loved one will diminish.

A relative who has observed this may then be able to help provide care for the patient without being frightened. It may help to give the relative a concrete task, such as cleaning the patient's tongue or keeping the lips damp, so that he understands there is something practical he can do for the dying person.

When a patient is in a coma, the physical care and pain control should continue in the same way as when the patient was still able to communicate verbally. It is important to remember that the patient is not only able to hear everything, but also to feel everything. The dying person experiences pain in the same way as before and, as we have discussed in a previous chapter, by observing his body language we can assess, for instance, whether he is comfortable or in pain, whether he is constipated or not. Body language will express not only his physical symptoms but also what is happening in his soul.

There are also physical signs to watch for. For example, when the patient has a brain tumor, one needs to check for severe headaches in which his facial features will be tense, as will be the expression of his eyes, and his face may be very red. It is desirable to check blood pressure daily. When a comatose patient begins to sweat profusely, this can indicate a heightened temperature or a sharp change in blood sugar levels which can be caused by some of the standard medications such as Dexamethasone.

Restlessness can be caused by physical problems such as a full bladder, severe constipation (even when a patient has not been eating for days, he still is in need of bowel care) or high blood pressure. Other problems can include headaches, nausea, pressure sores, or simply pain and discomfort from lying in an awkward position. Restlessness can sometimes be seen prior to death; there can be a resistance to letting go and this can take place on a physical as well as on an emotional and spiritual level.

The best we can do is to put ourselves in the patient's place: What would I want if I was lying there? The patient is not different from us, we are exactly the same.

In the hospice for some months we had Maxim, a sixteen-year-old who could not speak after a tracheostomy tube was inserted into his throat. Only through his eyes could he tell us what he wanted. His mother was unable to have real or meaningful contact with him, telling him the same stories and jokes over and over again. When she spoke to him, the words were always identical. Maxim seemed to be utterly frustrated by this and I felt it necessary to talk with him about what was going on inside. Looking into his eyes and at his body language I could see how deep his frustration was, not only with his illness but with all of us who did not understand what he was going through. I tried to put into words what he might be feeling: "Maxim, you cannot tell us what we are doing wrong, but I guess you would probably like to cry out something like this: 'Go away, I don't want you here, I've had enough of you all! I only wish I could shout at the top of my voice that you don't understand me!'"

Maxim listened to this slightly amazed, but nodded to let me know that this was precisely how things were. When a patient is unable to communicate verbally, either because of a stroke, throat cancer, tracheostomy, or a brain tumor, there is always a tendency to treat the person as a child who does not quite understand.

Even worse, the patient can easily be neglected, simply because he or she cannot ask for anything or complain. Patience has to be shown by the caregivers if they are to find out what the patient is trying to convey, whether in writing or through body language. At times, the best one can do is to sit with the patient and perhaps express amazement of the endurance the sick person is showing.

More than ever, respect and tact are needed in order to give the patient a sense of still being the same person. The sick person must be reassured that illness and the inability to communicate have not taken away his or her worth as a human being.

CHAPTER SEVEN

Family Relations and the Critically Ill Patient

We have already touched upon the fact that the patient and his relatives form a single reality. They are, so to speak, prisoners of each other's state of mind and heart. Those things (even if they are silent and unspoken) going on in the patient's soul and heart will be transmitted to close relatives, and vice versa. It is therefore important for the relatives to realize that an explosion of emotions may be a heavy burden to a patient who is perhaps barely coping with his physical decline and the fact that he is dying. If this is the case, I try to gently support the relatives and ask them to become more collected and still.

This process affects all levels of the sick person's being: physical, emotional, and spiritual.

A complex situation can arise when a patient is already dying but the relatives are insisting that their loved one should continue to eat and drink. At all costs, they want the patient to remain nourished. For relatives who are having difficulty accepting death, as long as a person is able to eat or drink, this is a sign of life!

Some relatives may accept that their loved one is dying, but the idea of withdrawing food, liquids, and even IVs can appear as a form of euthanasia, of the medical staff hurrying the patient out of this life. One has to explain to the relatives that during the process of dying, their loved one does not suffer from hunger, that the patient's organism can no longer digest food, and even drinking water can cause painful bloating as the organs can no longer pass liquid through the body. However, giving the patient a few small sips of something to drink, or simply moistening the lips and mouth is a good thing. By contrast, making the patient eat and drink will risk choking, and food or fluid can end up in the lungs.

On the emotional level, one sees how fussiness and unexpected disturbance can sometimes affect the patient, not only from relatives but by clumsy nursing. For instance, patients can be disturbed by sudden loud noises, such as a nurse's super-efficiency and brusqueness, loud conversation especially on cell phones, from television, or simply the door slamming. Suddenly switching on bright lights can upset a patient's precarious balance and sense of peace.

Another challenge for the relatives is to learn to gradually prepare during the loved one's illness to let him go: not to hold onto the patient at all costs and thus prolong his suffering. This greatly depends on their own outlook on life and death.

If they have deep, unresolved fears of death and separation, it may be difficult to let go of their loved one, and this may prevent him or her from dying in peace, as in this example:

Helen was admitted to the hospice in a very poor condition. Although her mother refused to accept that she was dying, Helen died almost upon arrival. At the moment of death, her mother fell upon her chest, screaming: "Lena! Lena! Breathe, breathe! Live, live!" And to my horror, with great difficulty and enormous effort, as if called back from a faraway depth, Lena once again took a breath. She opened her eyes, looked at her mother, and then, for the second time, died.

Here is another example:

Daniel was an educated man in his fifties with cancer of the bladder, whose condition was slowly growing worse. He was in the hospice many times for short periods and then discharged home again. By nature, he was a reticent, at times cynical, person. However, he eventually grew used to the people in the hospice, came to know the nurses, and opened up. One day, I asked him what had been the happiest period in his life. He answered with shining eyes: "My wife, my second wife Svetlana. I so much want you to meet her."

Unfortunately, Svetlana and I finally met only when Daniel was close to death. His wife was sitting next to him, it was already evening, and it seemed that she had a deep sense of guilt over not having come and visited him as often as she would have liked because of her work as the director of a large secondary school.

Svetlana did not feel at ease on this visit and asked me to stay with her. I also saw how Daniel could not find peace because he sensed Svetlana's pain and guilt. As a result, he became so tense that we were unable to control his pain. He was restless and kept looking at his wife. We all sat together for a couple of hours, and then I decided to tell Svetlana a story about a very ill woman whose husband could not find peace. Although he saw that his wife was suffering, he felt so guilty that he could not find the courage to let her go, to die in peace. He could not bear to be separated from her. Only after a very long time was he able to say to her, "I will let you go." And this was the moment that she finally was able to lie down in peace and die.

Late that evening, when I felt that Svetlana's inner turmoil had somehow subsided, I left them together. Daniel died that night and Svetlana was with him until the end. At the funeral, Svetlana asked me whether I remembered the story I had told her. I replied that, of course, I did. Then, she told me that after I left, she had sat at his bedside feeling so guilty that she did not know what to do. Then, in the middle of the night, she suddenly understood that the story I had told her was about herself. She continued, "Having asked him for forgiveness, I was able to say, 'Daniel, go in peace, I am letting you go.'" At that point he finally laid back quietly, his pain could be controlled, and after a little while he died peacefully.

CHAPTER EIGHT

The Hours Prior to Death

Very often, the relatives of a patient who is dying are at a loss about what to do. They may have deep fears of their own, and feelings of helplessness and vulnerability. On a practical level there is little to do, but the idea of simply staying quietly by the patient's bedside may be uncomfortable when accompanied by fear of the coming separation or of being alone in one's grief. I think that this situation is often more difficult for the relatives than for the patient who is dying. This is why one has to spend a great deal of time with the relatives, to get to know them and to make them feel that they are not in the way. On the contrary, they must be told that they matter as much as the patient does.

If the relatives are believers, the best thing they can do is to quietly pray for their loved one, asking Christ to be present. The only thing that is of no use at all, perhaps even counterproductive, is for an anxious relative to rattle off prayers in an agitated manner. This will convey their fear and anxiety to the patient rather than the depth and peace that should come with prayer.

When a patient is not used to praying, I don't believe that one should pray out loud or demonstratively without his or her consent because this can be frightening. One can always pray silently, holding the patient and all of the relatives before the face of God, and asking Him to support them in their suffering. To be present with an open heart and show readiness to be near as needed – to me these are the most important things.

From his long experience with seriously ill people, Vladika Anthony was of the opinion that dying alone is a terrifying prospect for most people. In his view, no one should die alone. If there are no relatives, then a doctor or nurse should stay with the patient right until the end.

Here is an extraordinary example of how it is possible to allay a patient's fear simply through one's presence:

Vladimir was twenty-four years old and the sarcoma on his arm had been treated with chemotherapy and two operations but to no avail. In spite of the obvious progression of his illness, his mother and older brother, Anatoly, kept pretending that all was going well. One day, as they repeated these empty words, Vladimir kept looking at me as if to ask, "Is this really true?"

None of them believed that life would continue after death. They all believed that death would be the end which, I think, frightened Vladimir even more. I told him about how in my family many people had already died, and how, to me, they were so alive. I gave him examples of what I had experienced myself and he listened rather eagerly but did not comment. Later on, when Vladimir's condition deteriorated, I asked his mother whether we should not discuss what was really going on with him. She did not agree with this because as it turned out, she had been diagnosed with cancer some years earlier and had herself a deep-seated fear of death from cancer.

Not long before his death, almost in a whisper Vladimir asked: "Am I dying?" I nodded and said to him: "At some point, yes, you will die, but be sure that you will not be left alone."

Towards the end, Vladimir became very short of breath, and as he lay dying, he was not left alone for a single moment. His brother Anatoly sat next to him, holding his hand, caressing him, and in a deep, calm voice, jokingly telling him: "*Volod*, no, that won't do, you need to breathe deeper, yes, like that, that's better... No, deeper, come on, you can do better than this."

While he was saying this, he kept looking at Vladimir, not taking his eyes off him for a moment. The gaze was silent, in the sense that nothing was said about the fact that Vladimir was dying, but Anatoly was using eye contact to send a message of comfort, as if to say: "Do not be afraid, we know what is happening, but I will not let you be frightened."

To me, it seemed as if Anatoly was spreading a veil of love over his brother that did not allow for any fear. This went on for many hours. His mother was there also, but I saw that in her agitation she was somehow left outside this magical circle of oneness. So, I asked her to moisten Vladimir's lips and to occasionally wipe his hands, so that she did not feel useless or excluded.

That same night Vladimir died; Anatoly stayed with him until the very end, keeping his brother relaxed and unafraid with his deep, calm voice, and their continuous (and it seemed to me, joyful) eye contact. This was such a beautiful example of sacrificial love, where the only thing that mattered was the patient's peace of soul.

CHAPTER NINE

After Death

After someone has died, one often senses a particular feeling of peace, a stillness which is not typical of life in general. At times one can see how pain and suffering have vanished from the patient's face and he has become younger looking. This is especially noticeable in children and young adults. When relatives and friends want to say goodbye to a person who has died, one has to warn them, especially if there are children present, that the person will be just the same, only that he or she will feel cold to the touch, as coldness is the mark of death, just as the mark of life is warmth.

There are people who are averse to seeing the person they love immediately after death, as if that person has changed in a terrifying way. This can be a sign of their own fear of or unfamiliarity with death, and may even have an element of superstition. Once I met a woman whose husband had died suddenly in the hospice. After he died, she continued to talk to him, and almost to accuse him of having left her and his young daughter. She told him he should not come and haunt them, and shouted: "What will your sister think of me? Will she accuse me of not having looked after you?" Often, in a state of shock, people talk about things which do not seem relevant, but this, I think, is an unconscious way of delaying the pain and sorrow.

The Body of a Person Who Has Died

The body of someone who has died is not just a garment to be thrown out. We have already talked about the body's role in human relationships when we express what is going on inside us through the way we walk, our tone of voice, our facial expressions, the look in our eyes, the tension in our muscles, and by how we touch others.

Vladika Anthony says the following:

> We know very well how our body's senses take part in everything that is going on in our mind and heart. A mother expresses her love to her child by touching and caressing him. How much comfort one can give by the touch of a hand and how much love, in all forms, can be expressed through the body. So, when we look at the body of someone who has fallen asleep, we do not simply look at a garment that we can dispose of, as many people try to convince themselves. At least, they say so in order to comfort themselves, to iron out the pain. The body is not a garment, we do not simply throw it away. This body is as real as the person is real, and is equally as real as our soul. Only in the oneness of the body and soul are we a full person.

Vladika Anthony continues,

> Yes, "me" is my body, just as "me" is my soul. One can see a person only in his wholeness, and this is why when we look at a body, we look at it with reverence. We look at this body with all of its suffering and its joy, the whole mystery of life that was embodied in this person. One could call the body the visible expression of the unseen.[33]

We have already talked about the close bond between the body and the soul that is clearly seen during life. When a person dies, his body is not a mere outer garment but remains the body of the person we loved and respected during life. The process of laying out a person who has just died, the washing of the body and putting on new clothes is an important part of the grieving process. In the Orthodox Church, we relate to the body of someone who has died

33 Antonij mitr. Surozhskij, "Zhizn'. Bolezn'. Smert': Smert." [Metropolitan Anthony of Sourozh, "Life. Illness. Death: On Death."] Ibid.

with reverence. During the burial service, the coffin is open, so that we can say our farewell to this person. This is necessary in order to fully realize that death is a real part of life.

Changes in the Body After Death

When I was twenty-two years old, I asked myself a painful question. I had returned from my summer holiday, and was told that a friend had died suddenly on a holiday in Italy. She was a medical student of my own age. To this day, I remember the corner of the street when we joyfully said goodbye to each other for the summer break, "Let's meet after we return!" Three weeks later, she had died of leukemia. I was shocked and devastated, and at the same time I could not stop thinking about what was happening to her body that had been so full of life but was now decaying. What troubled me most was what would happen to her eyes.

Many years later, I came across some words spoken by Vladika Anthony:

> On the one hand, we see that this body, so dear and precious, is conquered and defeated by mortality. On the other hand, we see in it a seed which has been sown, so that in the resurrection the body will rise again in all the splendor of immortality…. In our attitude towards the one who has fallen asleep, we must find a balance between the sight of decay and the certainty of eternal life, between the love for the place where the remains of a beloved body have been put to rest, and the certainty that our bond, our contact with each other, will continue in God for all eternity.[34]

To me, the place of burial and the grave itself, is a place to remember the person we love. That person is no longer there but rather alive in God. The grave should be respected and looked after, both as where the body is buried and in memory of our loved one,

34 ibid

and also to mark the day of their burial when we said our farewells. However, for some relatives there is a danger that the grave may almost become an idol. Other people can be trapped in a sort of unchanging photographic image of the last days of the beloved person's life, and are unable to look any further than the loved one's dying and death and the pain of separation. The fact that this person is now totally alive in God and has been fundamentally transformed, is often ignored. The person's sufferings have passed, everything that was such a torment to the dying patient and his relatives is simply not relevant anymore! To me it is tragic when people choose to remain trapped in the details of their loved one's death and the suffering prior to this.

It is not a coincidence that in the burial service of the Orthodox Church we sing: "Blessed is the way you are treading now, O soul, for a place of rest has been prepared for you, and my soul will be alive and will praise Thee, O Lord."

I would like to relate what Vladika Anthony's mother said to him just before she died, "If you never want to lose me, then do not come to my grave to meet me. Of course, that part of me that belongs to the earth will be lying there, and you can respect this place and look after it, but from now on we will communicate with each other not through our bodies; our communication will be in God."[35]

On the Resurrection of the Body

In one of his sermons, Vladika Anthony said,

> So often we think about death as the moment the soul will enter divine life and the body becomes dust. Yes, the body will turn to dust, but it has an eternal calling: the body will resurrect indeed, as Christ has risen, and one day we will all stand incarnate before

35 ibid

God with a transfigured body, as the transfigured body of Christ, with a soul which has been renewed through life eternal.[36]

None of this implies that it is an easy task to live through the death of a loved one. The pain of separation, of loss, of loneliness, are also an expression of our love, only this time not in joy, but in pain: they are the other side of the coin.

Vladika Anthony continues:

It speaks for itself that on the other hand there is the pain, the grief we are experiencing... the sorrow which is expressed in the name of the dying person in one of the troparions in the Canon for the Departure of the Soul: "Weep, sigh and lament, for I am now departing from you."

But this separation will only be temporary:

Together with this grief is also the certainty that is beyond any doubt, that death, which to us is loss and separation, means being born into eternal life, that death is a beginning and not the end. Death means the magnificent holy encounter between God and a living soul, which only in God will acquire its fullness.[37]

After someone has died, the relatives often have to face the acute and painful questions of "What now? How can I possibly continue with my life?"

As I see it, here again is a choice. One can become a victim of one's destiny, which entails an ever deeper sinking into grief and

36 Antonij mitr. Surozhskij, "Nedelya 6-ya po Pyatidesyatnice. Iscelenie rasslablenogo, voskresnaya propoved" ot 3 avgusta 1986 g. Voskresnye propovedi. Moskva: Novye mekhi, 2006 (Russian) [Metropolitan Anthony of Sourozh, "Healing of the Paralytic," Sunday sermon, August 3, 1986, 6th week after Pentecost]

37 Antonij mitr. Surozhskij, "Zhizn'. Bolezn.' Smert'.: Otpevanie" (Moskva: Fond Duhovnoe nasledie Mitropolita Antoniya Surozhskogo, 2010.) (Russian) [Metropolitan Anthony of Sourozh, "Life. Illness. Death: Burial." (Moscow: Metropolitan Anthony of Sourozh Spiritual Foundation, 2010).]

a complete closing down, or one can choose to courageously live through grief, accepting it as a process, as a journey in life that in the end will be enriching.

Even when there is pain and grief, I feel that one has to find definite tasks that will give meaning to life and may be an example for others. When this meaning has been found, it will help us not to be overwhelmed by grief or drown in self-pity.

CHAPTER TEN

Living Through Loss and Bereavement

How a person lives through bereavement, loss, and pain will to a great extent depend on his attitude toward life, suffering, and death. The relatives of the person who has died are going through the same stages (as described by Kübler-Ross) as the terminally ill patient did. However, it should be stressed that, as well as responding to their loved one's death through the successive phases of denial, anger, bargaining, depression, and acceptance, the relatives often suddenly come to another abrupt realization: that they themselves are destined to die as well. At some level everyone knows that death will come one day, but usually this thought has been comfortably shelved. Suddenly, this partial denial is no longer possible and, on the whole, the relatives' experience before and after a loved one's death can be even more difficult than anything undergone by the patient. This is why caring for the relatives is as important as looking after the patient.

About this, consider another quote from Vladika Anthony:

> We close our eyes in order not to see, because we are afraid to see what will happen. As a result, death appears unexpectedly and carries in itself not only the fright of its sudden appearance but an additional horror that strikes at the core of our vulnerability because the pain, the fear and horror has been growing and accumulating in us, but we refused to give them an outlet, we refused to mature.
>
> The blow is often more painful, more destructive, than if it had been an unexpected death, because apart from the horror, apart

from the bitterness of the loss, will also come the self-reproach and judgement for not having done what could have been done. We did not, because this would have asked of us to become real, to become honest without hiding from ourselves and the dying person that death was gradually opening its door, and that this door would one day open fully and the beloved person should have to go through it without looking back.

Each time we are faced with the slowly advancing loss of a person close to us, it is very important to look this in the face from the beginning, and to do this in perfect calmness, just as we look at a person while he is alive and with us. For thoughts about the coming death will stand against the reality of the person who is alive and present. We can be supported by this certain presence, while at the same time seeing ever more clearly the different sides of the coming loss. This is to balance between the certain present reality and the precariousness of thought, and allows us to prepare ourselves for the death of those who are dear to us.[38]

Viktor Frankl adds:

When a man finds that it is his destiny to suffer, he will have to accept his suffering as his task; his single and unique task. He will have to acknowledge the fact that even in suffering he is unique and alone in the universe. No one can relieve him of his suffering or suffer in his place. His unique opportunity lies in the way in which he bears his burden.[39]

For relatives, loss and separation are probably the most acute emotions that they experience. After the death of a dear one, this gaping hole, this desert of loneliness, is often very frightening to the people left behind.

38 Antonij mitr. Surozhskij, "Zhizn'. Bolezn'. Smert'. Starenie". (Moskva: Fond Duhovnoe nasledie Mitropolita Antoniya Surozhskogo, 2010.) (Russian) [Metropolitan Anthony of Sourozh, "Life. Illness. Death: Ageing." (Moscow: Metropolitan Anthony of Sourozh Spiritual Foundation, 2010).]

39 Frankl, p. 99.

In relation to this, I once again quote Vladika Anthony:

> As long as a person is ill, we are engrossed in thoughts and cares about him and we do everything in a collected and focused manner. Once the person dies, it often seems to those left behind that anything they do has lost its meaning. In any case, it does not have a direct aim, a center, a focus. Life, although it was heavy and crucifying, had its own rhythm, but now [it] is unstable. Loneliness also means that there is no one to talk to, no one to listen to, no one to give one's attention to, that there is no one to answer or react. It also means, very often, that thanks to the person who left us, we had some worth in our own eyes: we really meant something to him, he confirmed us in our being and in our meaningfulness.[40]

Immediately after someone has died, especially if this was a child, the grief can be overwhelming. If we are present when death occurs, any spoken word to the relatives will often be superfluous.

In my experience, the only thing one can offer is our silent presence as an expression of compassion. One has to be prepared to take a bereaved person as he or she is, accepting the way that they choose to express pain and grief.

To Vladika Anthony, pain and sorrow are the other side of the same precious coin: "We must be ready to encounter grief and pining: to meet face to face everything that is going on inside ourselves.... We must be ready to recognize that love can also find its expression in suffering, and if we state that we really love the person who has gone from this life, we have to be ready to love this person from the depth of our pain and suffering, just as we loved him in joy. This requires courage."[41]

It is especially important to discuss with relatives the danger of delaying the start of the grieving process. If this process is postponed, ignored, or suppressed – for instance, by the use of

---

40 Antonij mitr. Surozhskij, "Zhizn'. Bolezn'. Smert'.," ibid.
41 Ibid.

tranquilizers – it will be much more difficult to get in touch with one's grief later on.

A middle-aged acquaintance once told me the following story about himself:

> This man was happily married with three children when his wife suddenly died of a heart attack, and he was left alone to care for the youngsters. Not long after, his mother died in a car accident and when he found that he could hardly cope with grief and the demands of daily life, he began taking tranquilizers, a period which lasted for twenty years. As he explained, he felt that he had managed to cope with life, in a manner of speaking, but all the time he had not really been living. It was as if a thick blanket had been thrown over him, and this had prevented him from being in touch with himself and with reality.
>
> When he decided to get off the tranquilizers, he realized that his grief had gone down somewhere so deep that he could no longer get in touch with it. He felt that he had lost twenty years of real life, and as a result was suffering mood changes, from euphoria to deep depression, and at times, severe bouts of anger.

This is a telling example of how tranquilizers over a long period will deeply suppress the pain of bereavement. This stops one from living courageously through one's grief and makes it impossible to live life to the full in all of its depth. As the example shows, medication can suppress not only the emotion of pain and loss but all emotions.

Another danger is getting trapped in grief, which implies an unconscious refusal to live through it. Instead of moving forward and taking responsibility for one's attitude to grief in order to mature and grow, one becomes an eternal victim.

Choices always exist, even in such tragic situations. We can either shut ourselves up and fall into an existential vacuum or open up and find a meaning in our pain. This may include finding and putting into practice certain tasks whose accomplishment can be a gift to others.

Vladika Anthony says about this, "Everyone who lives is an example [of] how to live or not to live with dignity. We have to learn from each person, alive or dead, to avoid the bad and to follow the good. Everyone who has known the person who died has to ponder deeply on what stamp has been put on his own life by this person, what seeds have been sown, and then bring forth fruit."[42]

Therefore, one of the tasks for relatives after the death of a beloved person could be to highlight the best in him, that which was full of beauty. Then we can make the firm decision to continue to demonstrate precisely those qualities in the departed one that inspired us most, so that the world will not be deprived of this light.

A decision like this can prevent bereaved relatives from being trapped in grief. For the person left behind, trying to continue that which was best in the life of the departed one is a way of becoming one with the beloved individual. The fruit of this effort will then belong to both of them.

When a bereaved person has the courage to face sorrow in all of its depth without tranquilizers and to finally come through the experience, there comes a time when he will be able to support others who have yet to begin grieving. He has the right to talk about the ways in which one can face bereavement and loss since he has himself experienced it.

If the bereaved relative is a believer, one of his tasks could be to enter so deeply into prayer and silence, that in the depth of his soul he can stand in the presence of God and find his departed loved one, who is now alive in Him. According to Vladika Anthony, this is the only place where a person can really be at one with a beloved person who has fallen asleep.

However, this type of prayer demands that we be sober, collected, and face our grief more deeply than just on an emotional or

42 Antonij ng, "Zhizn'. Bolezn'. Smert.': Zhizn' usopshego kak primer" (Moskva: Fond Duhovnoe nasledie Mitropolita Antoniya Surozhskogo, 2010) (Russian) [Metropolitan Anthony of Sourozh, "Life. Illness. Death: Life of the Deceased as an Example" (Moscow: Metropolitan Anthony of Sourozh Spiritual Foundation, 2010).]

psychological level: to enter one's soul in silent pain and to wait for whatever will be given, without anticipating anything.

Kübler-Ross advised the bereaved never to want or to expect a "sign" from the other world, either in dreams, appearances, or in "answers to prayer." She was convinced that if it was needed, a sign would be given: "I am deeply convinced that we will get what we need. If it is not given to us to see our beloved departed ones in our dreams or in another way, this can be a test of our faith and trust. We will receive that which we need, [rather] than what we would like."

I remember Margareth, who had lost her eighteen-year-old son Alexis. She told me several times, not without pain and some envy: "I do not see Alexis, but he has appeared to Aunty Claire! Why does he not come to me?" It seemed to me that she even felt a bit offended.

As regards the length of the mourning period, Kübler-Ross said that relatives should have no specific expectations. They should not imagine that the bereavement will last forever, nor that it will come to an end after a certain period. In general, she advises people not to think too much about this kind of thing, but just to try to live the best one can: at times to cry, at times to be angry. As far as possible they should try to live as they did before, even if initially this might mean going through life in a rather mechanical way.

When someone has lost a loved one, I sometimes talk about the fact that every separation will be a temporary one, since love is a quality of eternal life.

Here, I quote the words of Vladika Anthony from one of his sermons:

> The Lord lived, died, and has risen; and the Lord Himself tells us that death is temporary, like sleep. He tells us that behind death stands life, in which the souls of men are already alive, a life which will also encompass our bodies on the day of the wonderful Resurrection.

However, we continue to say: "He has died, she has died." When we hear the words of the apostle: "I do not want you to be without hope, as others, who believe in death…" We hear these words, and nevertheless we "know," that before our eyes lies a person who has died, and we want to remain without solace…. We know that death exists, and we do not believe that there is life.

How strange and terrible, that the obviousness of death shields us from the reality of life! So, put this question to yourselves, each of you: How many times God has spoken to us about life, and how many times did we answer: "Yes, I know that death has been overcome, will be overcome" … and this does not only relate to the death of the body. If we could only have faith in life, we would believe that it is not the end when someone close to us, near to us, dies.

Our relationship with him, our life in relation to him, will continue. If we want to find a living person, we should not say "yesterday," or "once," or "in the past." We should not look back, but [rather] we should now live in this person, who is alive in this real life; we should wait for something bigger, not smaller.

This is the same in relation to emotional and spiritual appearances. It is so easy for us to say that someone has died, that our friendship has died, that love has died, that everything which was most precious between people has died.

When the Lord tells us that all this has only fallen asleep, has gone deep in hiding, but yet lives (for everything which "is": love, friendship, tenderness, is alive; the only thing that dies out is that which, on earth, already carries within itself the stamp of death and decay), we nevertheless say: "No, Lord, I know for sure that all of this has died at its root."[43]

43 Antonij mitr. Surozhskij, "Nedelya 24-ya po Pyatidesyatnice. Voskreshenie docheri Iaira voskresnaya propoved' ot 17.11 1968 g. Voskresnye propovedi" (Moskva: Novye mekhi, 2006) (Russian) [Metropolitan Anthony of Sourozh, "Raising of Jairus' Daughter," Sunday Sermon November 17, 1968, 24th week after Pentecost]

Vladika Anthony continues:

> If we look at our love and say that it belongs to the past, then this means that we do not believe that the life of the departed continues. However, then we will have to confess that we are not believers [but] atheists in the crudest sense of the word.
>
> If God does not exist, if there is no life in eternity, then the death which has happened will have no metaphysical meaning whatsoever. It is then simply a natural fact…. However, in any case, we will have to look squarely at our faith or at the lack of it, and then take a definite stand and act accordingly.[44]

I would also like to quote Dietrich Bonhoeffer, a German Lutheran pastor and theologian who was one of the founders of the resistance in Nazi Germany. He was imprisoned for many years, far from his friends, family, and his fiancé. These are the words he wrote to the young wife of a friend who also faced a long separation from her husband:

> Nothing can make up for the absence of someone whom we love, and it would be wrong to try to find a substitute: we must simply hold out and see it through. That sounds very hard at first, but at the same time it is a great consolation, for the gap, as long as it remains unfilled, preserves the bond between us. It is nonsense to say that God fills the gap: He does not fill it, but on the contrary He keeps it empty and so helps us to maintain our former communion with each other even at the cost of pain.[45]
>
> …The dearer and richer our memories, the more difficult the separation. But gratitude changes the pangs of memory into a tranquil joy. The beauties of the past are borne, not as a thorn in the flesh, but as a precious gift in themselves. We must take care

---

44 Antonij mitr. Surozhskij, "Zhizn'. Bolezn'. Smert'.: Smert'." [Metropolitan Anthony of Sourozh, "Life. Illness. Death: On Death." Ibid.]

45 Dietrich Bonhoeffer, *Letters and Papers from Prison* (Abridged Edition), London: SCM Press, 1981. p 5.

not to wallow in our memories or hand ourselves over to them, just as we do not gaze all the time at a valuable present, but only at special times, and apart from these keep it simply as a hidden treasure that is ours for certain. In this way the past gives us lasting joy and strength.[46]

Feelings of Guilt in Relation to the Departed

So often, after a close person has died, I hear people say: "If only...." or "I did not do all I could..." or "I am to blame...I did not realize..." and so on.

There is another rather specific set of circumstances in which guilt can arise. It quite often happens that a relative has been sitting day and night with the loved one because he wants more than anything to be with him until the very end. Then, when he goes out for just a few minutes, the patient dies. Indeed, I think that this is not a coincidence. So often the dying person seems to find it too painful for the relative to be present at the actual moment of his death. As a last gift to him, the patient wants to die "quickly" as it were, to spare the relative the actual moment of separation.

The opposite can also be true. Sometimes the patient cannot die while the relative is sitting next to him because the relative is not ready to let him go. By holding on to the patient, the relative is prolonging the suffering. There is no way the patient can die in peace while the relative is present.

When a patient has died "quickly" after a relative left him for a few minutes, the relative may feel guilty that, in the end, the patient died alone. It is necessary to talk to them, stressing the fact that this was perhaps the dying person's last gift. This is necessary to avert an irrational guilt that can haunt the relatives for the rest of their lives.

Kübler-Ross is of the opinion that such feelings of guilt are of no help to anyone. They will only lead to emotional disturbances, and if one does not shed them, the result will often be a physical illness.

46 Ibid., p 54.

In my experience, feelings of guilt can also be related to forgiveness. If a relative is a believer and knows that the departed one is alive in God, then of course it is possible to ask for forgiveness in prayer. As we have said in a previous chapter, this involves looking seriously at whatever stands between the bereaved and the departed, whatever is not resolved, and then asking forgiveness of the departed and forgiving them ourselves.

Death presents us with the terrible prospect that after a certain point it will be too late to correct certain wrongs, but this can also be a stimulus to act justly here and now. Vladika Anthony speaks about the feeling that one day "it will be too late" and the effect that this can have:

> Death can become for us a challenge that will allow us to grow to our full stature through the continuous striving to be all that we can be. The only time that we are left without hope to become better is when we do not try to do all that we should today.
>
> For Dostoyevsky in his novel *The Brothers Karamazov*, the meaning of hell can be summed up in two words: "Too late." Too late to speak the words which could have been said, too late to make a gesture that could express our relationship. This does not mean that there is nothing more that can be done, but it will be at a different, higher price, the price of a tormented soul.[47]

To illustrate this point, Vladika Anthony gave the following moving example of something that happened to a young man during the Second World War. At the front, this young man had fallen in love with a nurse named Masha and they decided to marry when the war ended. One day as he was firing at the enemy, the nurse suddenly jumped out of the trenches, fell, and he discovered that he had accidentally killed her. More than forty years later, he had not been able to find inner peace. He had gone to confession, had given alms in her name, had done everything he could, but

---

47 Antonij mitr. Surozhskij, "Zhizn'. Bolezn'. Smert'.: Smert'." [Metropolitan Anthony of Sourozh, "Life. Illness. Death: On Death."] Ibid.

had not found peace of soul. When he met Vladika Anthony, the archbishop asked him whether he believed that Masha was alive. He answered: "Yes, I do." Vladika replied, "You have turned to everyone, to all the people who did not suffer. Turn to Masha herself and ask her to forgive you, and if she will pray to God to send you His peace." That was exactly what this elderly man did as soon as he arrived home. A few days later he returned to Vladika Anthony, having changed completely; he had at last found peace.

This is one of the examples that shows that it is possible to turn to a person who has died and to ask for forgiveness, to make one's peace. However, this is not an easy path. Often it entails tormented feelings, deep prayer, and learning to be silent before the presence of God and the person concerned.

It is important to ask forgiveness from both sides *prior* to the death of a person we love. If this has not been done, then often there will be tight knots of unforgiveness that will prevent the dying person or the already departed one, as well as those left behind, from finding peace.

Some people feel guilty about experiencing any joy after the death of a beloved person, as if this will be a sign of unfaithfulness to the one who has gone.

In the words of Vladika Anthony:

> One should not artificially warm up in oneself grief and a dramatic feeling of another's death, thinking that if these feelings are not present you did not love this person. Grief should be flowing into something else; into a love which will never end, in the awareness, that, "I will also tread this way. There will also be a time when I will die, and what joy there will be in meeting each other again...." Then the grief will become brighter.[48]

Often, we may not know how to relate to or communicate with a person who has just lost someone dear. We may not be sure how to

---

48 Antonij mitr. Surozhskij, "Pastyr' u posteli bol'nogo iz gl. Materiya i Duh" [Metropolitan Anthony of Sourozh, "Pastoral Care of the Sick and Dying."], ibid.

behave, or perhaps there is a feeling of inadequacy, a fear of being hurtful, or simply not knowing how to give support. It seems to me that one can answer this with a simple question to oneself: What would I want if I were in this situation?

As I have said, in my experience the most important thing is to simply be there: to be present and let the person grieve as he wishes and behave as he wants to behave. Often, the person who is grieving would like to talk about the person who has died. Sometimes, he needs to go through all that has happened, and perhaps even express some feelings of guilt: "What if...?"

The things the bereaved person says may be very simple and perhaps even incoherent. At times he will be talking more to himself than to the listener. The main thing is to be still, to listen without any desire to give advice or to change the painful subject. There is no need to distract him. Clearly the subject is not too painful for him, as he brought it up himself. (If the listener wants to change the subject, this may reflect his or her own discomfort with the topic of grief.) A conspiracy of silence is a difficult and hurtful experience for a bereaved person. It is much better to express the pain with a good listener. For that reason, it is important to remember to phone the bereaved person, or to be there for him, to listen, and if necessary, to let him cry.

Kübler-Ross gives the following advice. One should not ask, "Can I do something for you?" or even worse say, "Ring me if there is anything I can do for you." (In practice, the person will never ring!) It is much better to simply come and do something concrete and practical. For example, one can do some shopping, bring over a cooked meal, or simply clean the children's muddy boots!

CHAPTER ELEVEN

The Death of Children

We have already discussed how children and young adults are often capable of sacrificial love, and how they can forget about themselves in order to prepare their parents for their coming death. They do not think primarily about themselves, about their illness, or about the fact that they will die soon. More than anything, they are concerned about how their parents will endure the pain of separation and loss. (This fear of separation is stronger than any of the other fears we spoke of earlier.)

In contrast, the influence of parents on their offspring in these tragic circumstances can sometimes be negative. I have frequently observed that the way parents respond to the illness and approaching death of one of their children can affect the whole family. Their reactions will spill over onto the younger generation, both the sick child and his or her siblings. This, in turn, will rebound on the parents and have a deep effect on their own physical and emotional state. In these tragic situations where a youngster faces terminal illness, I am convinced that care for the parents is almost more important than the care for the dying child.

As in this case:

I especially recall twelve-year-old Andrew who had gone blind because of a brain tumor. He stayed with us for over three weeks. When he was transferred to the hospice he was already in critical condition, but it took a very long time for him to die. I recall the next to the last evening: both of his parents sat next to him, one on either side. To me, Andrew looked as if he was crucified: he had his arms outstretched, one to his mother, one to his father. However, they were not at all ready to let him go.

Andrew was suffering, but also obviously sensed his parents' pain and agony. That evening he was already in a coma, but I had a distinct feeling that he was "seeing" and feeling everything. Deep in the night, his parents told me, they suddenly saw that Andrew was already invisibly entering the other world. This realization gave them the courage to let him go.

In her book *On Children and Death*, Kübler-Ross raises the question whether children somehow know about their coming death even if they have not been told. She was convinced that terminally ill children (perhaps not consciously but at some intuitive level) do understand this. This opinion was based on her lifelong experience with very ill and dying children, and her correspondence with thousands of parents who had lost their children.

Often, children will ask their parents something like, "Mama, am I dying?" When children sense that their parents are not able or willing to discuss this, they will find other ways of expressing what is on their minds. For instance, older children will write poems or keep a diary to write down their thoughts and feelings, or they will find someone to talk to outside the family.

This outside person can be a classmate or someone in the hospital ward. Kübler-Ross is of the opinion that every person, big or small, in this situation will need someone who is ready to lend a listening ear, to enter an honest conversation about what is happening. She is also convinced that all sick children sense that their parents are anxious and lie awake at night. She emphasizes that the parents should not hide these feelings from their children, not be falsely cheerful or smile when inside there are only tears and despair. It would be better, she says, if the parents could share their pain with their sick offspring; then the children could comfort them, hug them. This kind of communication prevents the formation of a negative wall of silence between parents and children.

I agree that this is necessary, because when everything becomes clear and there is no dishonesty between the different members of the family, the sick child will be able to relax. He or she no longer feels excluded, and that in itself may lead to an easing of physical symptoms. This, however, does not mean that the child should somehow feel responsible for the grief experienced.

In communication with children and young adults who are dying, perhaps the most important thing is to help them grasp the fact that life will continue, that death is not the end, and to help them have an inner sense of the presence of God so that they will understand that their illness is not a preparation for death, but for Life.

Children are often amazingly close to the other world, which is real to them even if they don't talk about it, or if their awareness of this reality is unconscious. The only thing that can remove this closeness is their parents' fear, which can affect their own attitude and frighten them.

In my experience, there is an unfortunate tendency to give children who are very ill anything they want, such as cell phones, iPads, expensive toys, and so on. All kinds of distractions are provided and any outing organized if only such a thing is possible. I have also seen situations in the hospice where the parents give in to the child's every whim and desire, and regrettably so do the medical staff.

More often than not, this will be an unconscious substitute for the things that really need to be done: talking over what is happening and creating a calm atmosphere where self-expression is possible for the sick child or teenager. Ideally, everything should be done with the support of relatives to make it possible for the dying youngster to open up and have honest conversations about whatever fears and anxiety they may have.

Large amounts of presents or very expensive ones can reflect an awkwardness on the part of the donors that they do not know what else to do, and this excessive generosity may be a kind of defense against the hard facts of terminal illness. It seems to say, "Let's try to soften this uncomfortable situation with gifts and distractions," ignoring the need to find one's own attitude to suffering. If gift-giving masks an inability to communicate, the child or young adult may face death without meaningful support.

In any situation where excessive giving of gifts occurs, it would be good for parents and medical staff alike to ask themselves why they are "spoiling" the child in this way. Is it for the child's benefit or their own reluctance to face the complexity of suffering and death, especially in young people?

The death of a child is a great tragedy for all the family members, and this creates a strong reason for everybody, including the youngster whose life is ending, to courageously face this together.

Children's Fear of Death

Kübler-Ross is of the opinion that very small children have only two types of fear: the fear of sudden loud noises and the fear of falling. As the child grows up, a different fear emerges, that of separation from parents, the fear of abandonment, or worry that a loving parent will suddenly be absent. This is why one or both parents should always try to be with the child when he or she is in the hospital, and the staff should see that parents have unhampered access to the child.

According to Kübler-Ross, in addition to the fear of separation, children age three or four will experience a fear that their body will be mutilated, or that something physically unpleasant will happen. Children may have a limited experience of death, such as having seen how a cat has killed and eaten a mouse, and can identify death with physical trauma.

Apart from this, children of this age have also discovered that they have a body and are proud of it. Little boys, according to Kübler-Ross, want to be big and strong; little girls want to be pretty. That is why children of both sexes fear that medical procedures (such as injections) will somehow distort their bodies. About this, Kübler-Ross gives the following advice: when certain unpleasant medical procedures have to be performed, the parent should in no way try to calm the child with promises of a reward; for example, a toy or sweets. Children will quickly understand that the more they cry, the greater their reward will be. Instead, one should always tell the truth about what is happening. For example, we can use a doll or a soft teddy bear to prepare the child and demonstrate what will happen.

What about children's attitude to mortality? To children of four or five, it seems that death is a temporary phenomenon. A five-year-old child can say that she "wishes her mother were dead" after she has been scolded for bad behavior. However, a couple of hours later she wants her mother to be alive again and to play with her.

Kübler-Ross gives as an example the words of her four-year-old daughter, who after the death and burial of her little dog said, "Oh, this is not so terrible, for in the spring he will come alive again, just like the tulips do." In the writer's opinion, one should not take away this faith or try to convince the child that no such thing will happen.

In my own experience, older children from the age of five until the teens can accept the reality of death with remarkable calmness. They are not terribly frightened. It is the parents' fear which can have a negative influence on them and on their feelings about the prospect of death.

Here is an example:

Although he knew he was dying of a brain tumor, six-year-old Peter had no fear of death. His mother told me that one day while he was being treated in the hospital, Peter had suddenly looked up at the hospital ceiling and obviously had a conversation with someone. When his mother asked him who he'd been talking to, he simply said: "St. Daniel of Moscow!" When she asked him what the holy man looked like, Peter said: "Oh, so beautiful, he is all white and young." When she asked him what the saint had told him, he replied, "He told me I need not be afraid because he would be waiting for me."

Neither of them had previously known of this saint, and for Peter's mother it was a great comfort to know that after his death, her child would not be alone, but met by this saint. It was a clear sign to her that life continues after death.

The Suffering of Siblings

The brothers and sisters of a dying child also need support. Without it, they can behave aggressively or cruelly, and at times they may even say (or feel, without saying it) something like: "I just wish he would die." Kübler-Ross sees this as a clear indication that these siblings need more attention. In no way should they be punished for saying such things but rather given the opportunity to vent their fear and emotions, including feelings of being abandoned. Sibling anger can show that they are feeling neglected themselves, as if, for their parents, they hardly count. At times, they wish that their brother or sister would die soon, simply because they want life to go back to normal, as it was before. When the death finally does take place, they can have a feeling of guilt and fear, and this must be attended to.

Kübler-Ross gives a great deal of attention to the question of whether one should allow siblings to be around the dying child. She concludes that it is important to let them participate as much as they are able in the care of their sick brother or sister. For example, they could have a concrete task, such as bringing the family dog or cat along for a visit, offering food or drinks, playing with the sick child on the computer, or listening together to music. They need to do this naturally and remain themselves, just as they are, without any fear or feeling of awkwardness.

She also talks about the feeling of guilt that parents may have if they allow themselves a moment of enjoyment when their child is ill. In her view, the mother should not lose herself totally in the care of her child; she should go to the hairdresser, to lunch, enjoy a film. She should also attend to the rest of the family because nothing is worse than creating a heavy hospital atmosphere at home. As long as the child is alive, there should be laughter and joy around him. In a word, everyday life should go on.

Kübler-Ross also was of the opinion that there is no need to constantly watch over or tiptoe around the child who has a terminal illness. The child may wonder, "Why did I not get such attention and so many presents before I got ill? Did I mean less to them than now?" He may feel that he himself is not worth much except in the context of his illness.

She gives an example of a little boy with cancer whose parents gave him everything he wanted. The child began to demand more and more expensive toys, as if he was testing them. Could he get anything he wanted or was there a limit to it? His brother watched this in amazement, then with jealousy and resentment. He also asked for a present and the answer was: "We have no money for this." "Then why do you buy presents for my brother?" To which the reply was, "And you, would you also like to have cancer?"

So, the brother understood that only when you are ill, do you get such presents. After a while he developed asthma, then he started bedwetting. When Kübler-Ross met him, she asked how he was getting on and he answered her, "You know, I have asthma, but I do not think that this is enough." Through this example it is clear that no matter what age they are, siblings can have as difficult a time as the parents and even the dying child.

In an example from our own hospice, there was a young woman named Tanya.

She was very talented, and excelled in photography. She also played the guitar very well and obviously had been the pride and joy of the family prior to her illness. Her younger brother, Alexis, had clearly lived in the shadow of his talented sister. The mother adored Tanya, and she seemed to live only for her.

It was painful to observe how Alexis could not do anything good for his mother while Tanya was dying. The boy tried his utmost to comfort her, but the mother would not let him come close. She told me somewhat negatively: "Oh, he is only good at computers." After Tanya died, she fell into a deep depression; she only wanted Tanya back, nothing else, and kept asking: "Why her?" When I looked at Alexis, I had an acute sense of how much suffering there can be for the siblings in a family with a dying child.

When siblings are given concrete tasks to help care for the sick family member, they will be less frightened and traumatized as their brother or sister get worse. Children observe all that is happening with different eyes and they communicate on another level. However, if the siblings have not been taking part in the care of their sick brother or sister, one has to prepare them before they come to visit by telling them what is happening and how the appearance of their sick family member will have changed.

This applies to all children who face the death of a close relative, as we can see here:

In our hospice, Svetlana, a mother of two young children, was dying.
The eldest daughter, aged nine, had visited her mother often, including the day before she died. The youngest, Rebecca, who was only four years old, had been to the hospice rarely and had not seen her mother for a while.

When Svetlana died, I said to her husband, John: "If I can be of help in any way, please let me know." The next day he rang to ask my support in telling the youngest daughter that her mother had died. John told me that he wanted to tell her that Mommy had gone to Paris or that she had died and turned into a butterfly! To this I replied: "No, that is not a solution, such a falsehood is not facing the problem, and besides, every butterfly would be identified with their mother." The difficulty was that I had not yet met Rebecca, and when I came to their home, I found a very lively little girl looking at me inquisitively. The father left us alone, expecting me to tell Rebecca about her mother's passing.

I was not at all sure how to approach the subject, since I did not know the child, so I sat down and asked her to draw me her family and the house they were living in. Rebecca, I felt, would have rather continued playing than to draw for me, but she agreed to this if I, in exchange, would draw her a cat. When I had done this, she looked at my cat and said disdainfully: "How ugly!" Then she quickly drew me a picture of her family. Her mother was not there. When I asked her where her mother was, she said angrily: "She's in the hospital. Ugh, I don't like it, she vomits." Then at my request she reluctantly drew a picture of her mother. To my astonishment, she portrayed her mother with her stomach as a big red circle and her head in a green circle with an enormous cross in it.

Rebecca almost threw the picture at me and ran off to her father. When I showed it to him, he said he was now ready to face the task himself, and would tell Rebecca about her mother's death later that night.

The Last Farewell to a Child Who has Died

Kübler-Ross feels that when a child is dying, ideally, the whole family should be present. All of the siblings have a right to be there and take part in what is happening. She says there are many families who pray or sing some well-loved songs together when there are no other visitors. Once the child has died, she writes, the parents can take the child in their arms, wash them, and, if possible, carry him or her to the mortuary themselves. This is the concrete, practical beginning of the bereavement process.

Kübler-Ross warns against the impulse that some people have to move house soon after the child's death, so that nothing will remind them of the tragedy. One has no real choice but to live through one's grief to the end. Besides, she says, to stay in the same house will be a solace for the other children; they have already gone through such turmoil that moving house would mean extra stress for them.

There is an opposite danger in making a shrine out of the child's room after their death. Kübler-Ross says that one should resist the impulse to preserve the place unchanged with its memories of the child or to make it a space that is completely static. On the other hand, the desire to remove all pictures of the child is another extreme. She feels that one should concentrate on life and on all of the people who are alive but not deny or hide the fact that the child existed.

Often the question is asked if the siblings should come to the funeral. Kübler-Ross is of the opinion that the children should not be stopped from saying their last farewells, for without this it will be difficult to let go of the one who has died with one's whole heart. Funerals, she says, are also a means of letting the public know of our grief and of proclaiming that this person has been dear to us and has played an important role in our life.

However, if the bereaved sibling is troubled by too many unresolved and contradictory issues in relation to the one who has died, this may find expression in their refusing to attend the funeral. This has to be taken seriously, for often it indicates that the child needs help.

Siblings need not be forced to be at the funeral if they manifestly don't want to go. Otherwise it is sensible to encourage any willingness they show to attend, and to let them know that this is the right decision.

She goes on to say that whenever there is a significant event in the family, whether it be a happy or a tragic one, the family should live through this together. When a sibling refuses to go to the funeral, this is perhaps indicative of fear, of a feeling of shame, or of hidden grudges against the departed child or the parents. Before the funeral, all of this should be discussed with the brother or sister with understanding and love, without judgment.

Kübler-Ross is also of the opinion that if we always behaved in this way, there would be much less need for our children to seek psychological support later on in life. Drawing on her experience, she feels strongly that a grown-up should bring the children to the brother or sister who is lying in an open coffin, and that any question should be permissible. The bereaved child should also be allowed to touch the family member who seems to have fallen asleep. Ideally, this grown-up person should not be a parent but rather a close friend of the family, someone the sibling trusts and feels comfortable with. This is for the simple reason that a parent's emotions will interfere with those of the bereaved child.

Vladika Anthony was also of the opinion that children should be allowed to see and say their farewell to the departed person who has been laid out in an open coffin, as is the practice in the Orthodox Church.

It is important, he says, for parents to explain to the child ahead of time that the departed is the same person, but with a difference. He will feel cold to touch, since this is the mark of death, as the mark of life is warmth. One has to warn about this, otherwise it can be a sudden shock for the child when he stretches out his hand to the beloved family member.

It is Kübler-Ross's experience that very often the children want to touch the departed and to leave a little present or a small letter. One can also discuss with them the fact that this person who has gone to another world is really still alive. This means that the departed one will hear and understand anything they tell him; he will help them in their pain, and through this, those left behind, both young and old, will sense their never-ending closeness.

Conclusion

The subject of this book is about preparing a person for Life, not for death. It is impossible to prepare someone for death, because we ourselves have no experience of it. What we can do, according to Vladika Anthony, is to prepare someone for Life. In order to live life to the full in all its depth, without fear or defenses, and in a spirit of readiness to take risks, one needs inner support. This can be an ideal which is so important that it transcends one's own situation. It may be a deep and real love for a person, or for God.

Without this inner support, any serious crisis will be difficult to face and to live through courageously. The final and perhaps most difficult crisis that each of us will face is coping with the prospect of serious illness and death.

This book has dealt not so much with death itself as with the complex and dramatic processes (physical, emotional, and spiritual) that are connected with our passing over to the next world. Suffering, illness, and dying are an integral part of our life, an extraordinarily important part that needs to be understood and accepted. Vladika Anthony says: "We cannot deal with this question if we do not have our own position, our own criteria towards suffering and death. Often fear of suffering is worse than the suffering itself."

Each person needs to develop a way of understanding, a fundamental attitude to suffering and death, especially as it affects oneself. When this is not done, people often put up powerful "defenses" against these painful realities which may vary from a denial of the diagnosis to a total denial of the coming death. This in turn can lead to a web of untruths, which will stand between the terminally ill patient and his or her relatives. As a result, the dying patient is left to face the end of life alone, without real emotional or spiritual support. Several cases have been described in which the patient's pain, at every level, could not be alleviated because of this conspiracy of denial.

In this book, I have often quoted Metropolitan (Vladika) Anthony of Sourozh. His experience as a medical doctor, psychiatrist, and priest has been of invaluable help to me in clarifying and illustrating the issues dealt with in this book. For the same reasons, I have quoted the psychiatrist Elisabeth Kübler-Ross, as well as Viktor Frankl and Etty Hillesum, both of whom testified by their presence in the German concentration camps about the possible dignity and calling of man.

The conclusion that I myself can draw after so many years of treating and looking after terminally ill patients and their relatives is that there are always choices to be made, however tragic the circumstances. This includes the chance to outgrow one's weaker self and live to the end in a dignity that is worthy of our calling, and to take responsibility for one's attitude towards life, including illness, suffering and death, rather than getting stranded in self-pity and as passive victims of "fate."

We have discussed the heroic tenaciousness that can be shown by a dying person in tragic and cruel circumstances, and how, despite everything, this person can acquire the ability to live (during whatever time remains) for someone or something higher than themselves.

Those friends and relatives left behind are no less in need of the inner support that comes from developing a balanced and conscious attitude to life, suffering, and death. Here also is a choice: either to move towards the light, towards personal growth via the painful process of going through this loss and separation, or to close down into oneself and one's pain, and prevent the soul from growing and maturing.

This is a book about Life, the essence of which is the sacrificial love that is ultimately God's own love. This love shows itself when a person's heart is open to the pain of another human being without fearing or avoiding the sufferer's agony.

However, this type of love requires of us sobriety and courage. It essentially demands an opening of the heart, as opposed to staying close and safe in one's shell. It is precisely this openness of heart, this ability to show real compassion which places the patient and relatives in the very center, which in my opinion should be the core of any medical treatment and procedure.

This openness of heart is needed not only for the doctors and nurses but equally for the patient and relatives, as they too must take responsibility for developing a right attitude towards life, illness, and death.

Only with an open heart will one be able to see what is really happening behind the deceptive appearances and masks, and to act accordingly. The words spoken by Saint-Exupéry's *The Little Prince* come to mind. He says that what is real is invisible to the eyes, that it is only with the heart that one can see clearly.

Vladika Anthony discusses this in a similar way, and I would like to end with his quotation:

> Everything passes; in the end only one thing will remain – a living heart that no one can kill unless we ourselves close it, and then it will lie as a heavy stone in our chest.
>
> But if we open our heart, if throughout our life we accept every joy, every suffering, every sorrow, every pain – if we are not afraid to live through pain and suffering right up until the end... if at no moment we cry out: "No, enough," but say: "Lord, Thy will be done," then our heart will be ploughed, it will be able to love unconditionally. Then, depending upon how much the sensitivity of the heart grows, there will be in equal measure a growth of wonder before God and before life, and an infinite gratitude for everything....
>
> God does not pull us out of earthly sorrows, out of life, where joy and grief alternate with one another. He acts like this so that our heart will become deep and that an unshakeable love can nestle in it, so that in our soul, in our life, nothing will remain but love. The Lord is also saying to us: "Do not cry." Not that He is asking us to forget our sorrow, but that through our faith in Him, in our certainty of things invisible, we will outgrow

ourselves, outgrow time, outgrow sorrow, and will mature into a real and true person. Such a person will be capable of living his life in love equally for the living and for those who have fallen asleep. There will be no difference because on earth love will never end, and after death, love will become unshakeable.[49]

49 Antonij mitr. Surozhskij, "Poslednee soderzhanie zhizni. Puti christianskoj zhizni," (Besedy. Kiev Duh i Litera, 2001) (Russian) [Metropolitan Anthony of Sourozh, "Christian Ways of Life: The Last Content of Life" (Talks. ed. Kiev, 2001 from Nativity Retreat, January 3, 1976, London).]

About the Author

In 1988, Frederica de Graaf qualified as a specialist in acupuncture after a four-year course of study at the University of Oriental Medicine (ICOM) in East Grinstead, England. For twelve years she had her own clinic in London, where she treated patients of all ages with many different illnesses and complaints.

In 2001, with the blessing of Metropolitan Anthony Bloom, she moved to Moscow where she received her second higher education in psychology. From 2002 to the present she has worked as an acupuncturist and psychologist at the First Moscow Hospice.

Over many years Frederica has attended conferences and seminars in different parts of Russia and Georgia, lecturing to medical staff, clergy, monastics, social workers, and psychologists on the complex issues related to death and dying in terminal care.

At present, she also teaches psychology students at the Moscow Orthodox University of St. John the Theologian.

Not long before his death Metropolitan Anthony told Frederica: "You know, there will never be a separation, not with you or with any of our parishioners." This was their last meeting; within five months he had died. Since then almost fifteen years have passed but Frederica knows from experience that his words are true: there is no separation in death.

Bibliography

Metropolitan Anthony of Sourozh

1. "Human Values in Medicine," *Bristol Medico-Chirurgical Journal.* 1974. Vol. 91 (1-2) pp 3-7.

2. "On Death," from the website of Metropolitan Anthony of Sourozh. Archive: http://masarchive.org/Sites/texts/1978-00-00-1-E-E-T—EW00-010OnDeath.html

3. "On Facing Suffering" an address given in the University Church of St. Mary the Virgin, Oxford, February 1, 1969.

4. "Zhizn'. Bolezn'. Smert,'" Moskva: Fond Duhovnoe Nasledie Mitropolita Antoniya Surozhskogo, 2010 (Russian) ["Life. Illness. Death." Moscow: Metropolitan Anthony of Sourozh Spiritual Foundation, 2010. (Talks given by Metropolitan Anthony on April-May, 1984 at the Russian Cathedral in Ennismore Gardens, London.)]

5. *Stupeni: O bolezni dushevnoj i telesnoj, Besedy Mitropolita Antoniya Surozhskogo, Reshma: Izd. Makariev-Reshemskoj Obiteli,* 1998. (Russian) [Steps: About Mental and Physical Illness, Talks by Metropolitan Anthony of Sourozh. (Ivanovo, Edition of Makaryev-Reshemsky Monastery, 1998).]

6. *Besedy na Evangelie ot Marka:* "Nachalo Evangeliya Christa, Syna Bozhiya..." Moskva: Danilovskij Blagovestnik,1998 (Russian) [*Talks on the Gospel According to Saint Mark:* "The Beginning of the

Gospel of Jesus Christ, the Son of God." *Danilovsky Evangelist*, Moscow, 1998.]

7. "Dialog veruyushchego s neveruyushchim." Besedy s A.M. Goldbergom v religioznoj programme Bi-Bi-Si" (1972) (Russian) ["Dialogue of a Believer with an Unbeliever" for BBC religious program. London, 1972.]

8. *Chelovek pered Bogom*, Moskva: Fond Duhovnoe Nasledie Mitropolita Antoniya Surozhskogo, 2010 (Russian) [*Man Before God*. Moscow: Metropolitan Anthony of Sourozh Spiritual Foundation, 2010.]

9. "Body and Matter in Spiritual Life." *Sacrament and Image: Essays in the Christian Understanding of Man.* Ed. A. M. Allchin, Fellowship of St. Alban and St. Sergius, London, 1967.

10. "Pastyr' u posteli bol'nogo iz gl." *Materiya i Duh*, Trudy: v 2-h kn. Kn 1 Moskva: Praktika, 2002. (Russian) ["Pastoral Care of the Sick and Dying." ed. Praktika, Moscow, 2002] Talks with Fr. Sergei Hackel for BBC Russian religious program «Resurrection» October 1993 – January 1994, London.

11. "Nedelya 6-ya po Pyatidesyatnice Iscelenie Rasslablenogo," Voskresnaya propoved ot 3 avgusta 1986, Novye Mekhi, Moscow, 2006. (Russian) ["Healing of the Paralytic," Sunday sermon August 3, 1986 Sunday of the 6th Week after Pentecost]

12. "Nedelya 24-ya po Pyatidesyatnice. Voskreshenie Docheri Iaira," Voskresnaya propoved ot 17.11.1968 Moskva: Novye Mekhi, 2006. (Russian) ["Raising of Jairus' Daughter," Sunday sermon November 17, 1968, 24th week after Pentecost.]

13. Poslednee soderzhanie zhizni. Puti christianskoj zhizni: Besedy. Kiev: Duh i Litera, 2001. (Russian) ["Christian Ways of Life, The Last Content of Life," Talks ed. Kiev, 2001.] Nativity Retreat, January 3, 1976, London.

Bonhoeffer, Dietrich, *Letters and Papers from Prison* (Abridged Edition), London: SCM Press, 1981.

Frankl, Viktor E., *Man's Search for Meaning*. New York: Washington Square Press, 1985.

Hillesum, Etty, *An Interrupted Life: The Diaries, 1941-1943*. New York: Pantheon Books, 1983.

Hillesum, Etty, *Une vie bouleversée: journal 1941-1943 suivi de lettres de Westerbork,* (Trad. de Nederl. P. Noble) Paris: Ed. de Seuil, 1991.

Kübler-Ross, Elizabeth, *On Death and Dying,* Abingdon-on-Thames: Routledge, 1969.

Pogrebin, Letty Kottin, *Ispytanie bolezn'yu.* (Moskva: Livebook, 2014.) p. 99. [*How to Be a Friend to a Friend Who's Sick.* (Moscow: Live Book, 2014) p. 99.]